QIGONG ~ MASTERING YOUR OWN PRACTICE GROUP

Simple Methods to Start, Build, and Host a Qigong Practice Group

GoldenPhi Press, LLC

Minnesota

Copyright © 2016 Jim Cormican
All rights reserved.

ISBN: 978-0-9863928-1-8

"The information presented in Jim Cormican's new book "Qigong – Mastering Your Own Practice Group" helps guide and empower the new as well as the experienced teacher with valuable tools and insights on how to start their own group. I have had a good look at it and passed it around to a few of my senior students.

We are all impressed with the work you have put in and the attention to detail. **It really is a complete guide on how to start and run a successful Qigong group. Some of this information my teachers shared with me and some I worked out over the last twenty five years of my teaching career.** Thank you for putting this information together, I think we all can benefit by providing a secure, nurturing professional environment allowing our students to connect with their Qi and improve their quality of life."

Simon Blow
Author, Publisher and Producer
Classes, Workshops/Retreats and China Qigong Study Tours
25th Generation Dragon Gate Daoism
29th Generation Da Yan - Wild Goose Qigong
Deputy Secretary
World Academic Society of Medical Qigong, Beijing, China
www.SimonBlowQigong.com

"The National Expert Meeting on Qi Gong and Tai Chi identified the need for experienced practice leaders to disseminate Qigong in communities throughout the U.S.

Cormican's book is a **timely instruction manual which addresses this need by providing a wealth of information based on his own experience that people can use to start and maintain their own Qigong practice groups.**"

Tom Rogers
President and CEO
The Qigong Institute
www.QigongInstitute.org

"This guide **contains valuable tools and information for getting your practice group off the ground** and running for many years to come"

Brian Trzaskos
PT LMT CSCS CMP MI-C
Institute for Rehabilitative Qigong & Tai Chi
www.IRQTC.org

This book is dedicated to...

My Lovely Wife Maureen, to Whom I Thank for all the Wonderful Years of Support and Experiences, for Showing me the Deeper Understanding of the Meaning of the word Family, and Increasing the Number of Relatives in our Family.
Many Whom I Love Dearly.

My Friends Rich Muller, John Grozik, and Cliff Allen, in their Support for Many Years Past in Helping me Get to Where I am Today, along with the Great Journeys we Have Shared.

My Raelyn Rose – The One Who Makes My Heart Soar like an Eagle Every Time I See Her.

Mr. Dog, for his Many Years of Dedicated Service to the Family, for Being a Great Trooper, and Someone Who Will be a Treasured Memory. He Will be Greatly Missed.

All Those Who Practice Qigong.

GoldenPhi Press, LLC – Minnesota
www.GoldenPhiPress.com

Ordering Information and Customizing for Your Students:
Special discounts are available on quantity purchases by corporations, associations and others.

Organizations can add their style of Qigong (photos of exercises, tips, experiences, etc.), into this book and redistribute to their own students. For details, contact the publisher at the website above.

Qigong ~ Mastering Your Own Practice Group:
Simple Methods to Start, Build, and Host a Qigong Practice Group
by Jim Cormican

ISBN 978-0-9863928-1-8

Cover Design by Jim Cormican
Edited by Maureen Donovan-Cormican
Illustrations by Jim Cormican
Interview of Mr. Cormican by Raelyn

Published & Printed in the United States of America
First Edition: January 2016

The books focus is on providing quality and reliable information in the topics covered. The information provided herein is stated to be straightforward and consistent, and under no circumstances will any legal responsibility or blame be held against the publisher or the author for any reparation, monetary loss, or damages due to the information herein, either directly or indirectly.

Although the author and publisher have made every effort to ensure that the information in this book was correct at press time, the author and publisher do not assume and hereby disclaim any liability to any party for any loss, damage, or disruption caused by errors or omissions, whether such errors or omissions result from negligence, accident, or any other cause. The material herein is offered for informational purposes only.

Recording of this publication is strictly prohibited and any storage of this document is not allowed unless with written permission from the publisher.

If you find any errors in this book, please email the editor at:
MasterQigongGroups@GoldenPhiPress.com

Contents

THANK YOU

There is so much involved in writing a book. Research, planning, putting your thoughts on paper, cover designing, tons of rewrites, organizing, editing, and then trying to read chicken scratch notes weeks or months later, wondering what you were trying to say. This little project took about four years. But during this time, it brought some wonderful people with great talent and wisdom into my life. So I would like to give thanks to those around me who took the time to help me in my venture to bring my thoughts and vision to full fruition. I would deeply like to thank those who contributed in looking over my notes, provided wordsmithing, encouragement, and looked at things from a different perspective to eliminate confusion with my readers. Here are those who helped make it possible for you to enjoy this book. Without them, this would have not been in your hands.

My wife Maureen for the many long hours she contributed correcting the grammatical errors and rewording my thoughts so others can understand my thinking process. She is very talented and gifted in this area where I am not. She's the best in the business and I learned a lot from her. With her busy schedule, along with taking care of our granddaughter, she multi-tasked to keep the data dust from collecting on my work.

My best friend and mentor, Rich Muller, who has been there for me during the days of one of my companies, from startup to reaching the heavens and sharing that joy with me. A very good friend for many years who took the time to review my first draft and made suggestions in organizing it and provided me with very useful advice in marketing.

My good friend Barb Palmer, who took the time from her adventurous trips to Arizona (experiencing those wonderful energy vortexes), read my book cover to cover and consulted me in the areas of Qigong to make sure the information was accurate. She provided great insight on things that I did not know and helped me eliminate some of the confusion. She was my first teacher, and I continue to learn from her to this day.

And to those whom took time out of their busy schedules and allowed me to interview them about their experiences for this book. Barb, Arda, Gadu and Bruce. Thank you for allowing me the pleasure to hear your wonderful stories and letting me share them with my readers. You all provided some great insight into your world of Qigong and your practice groups. I know your stories will inspire, educate and provide ideas to those who are currently leading or thinking about starting a practice group.

I would also like to say thank you to Pathways Minneapolis for providing tools in helping my family cope with the many unexpected changes in our lives. They are some wonderful people along with those that attend. We've made some great friends there.

I would like to say many thanks to all of you in making this dream become a reality, continuing the spirit of Qigong, and helping others.

PREFACE

Dear Qigonger,

This book is not designed to teach you how to do Qigong, or talk about the type of Qigong that I have learned and practiced over the years, but a guide to help you build, facilitate, and grow your own Qigong practice group. Or if you have become a master yourself of Qigong and you are looking for ways to bring success to your student's practice groups, this would be an indispensable guide for them. This manual has been written to be used for any form of Qigong that you practice and teach others. You may even use some of the information presented here for other arts that you may teach like Tai Chi or Yoga. The information contained within these pages are an excellent baseline to get you started, but applying your imagination can bring great results for you and your group.

I have incorporated tips and techniques that I have learned while I have been teaching, along with advice from others who run their own practice groups. I will also share some of their stories and experiences with you. There is also a web link that accompanies this book so you can download documents to help grow your Qigong practice group. There will be more information in the back of this book on how to do this and also what is available.

There is also a website called Qigong with Jim & Friends (www.QigongWithJim.com) that was created as a tool for you so that you can post your own Qigong Practice Groups, send out announcements to your own members, find other practice groups, have people RSVP for your events, mingle with others who also teach, ask questions from others to help further your own group(s), share your own stories, and much more. It is a website built on much love with the focus on socialization to connect people from around the world to help each other, build relationships, and bring knowledge to you in building your practice group(s). You can also find additional material that was not be mentioned in this book, but posted by me or other Qigongers who participate on the website.

A blog has been created as a continuation of this book, you can find it online at Blog.QigongWithJim.com where you can grab more tools and techniques on leading your Qigong practice groups.

You can start anywhere inside this book. It was written so that you can quickly find the information you need and not overload you with content that is fluffy, unrelated, or filler to add more pages. It contains short chapters that are straight to the point to get you the content you need so you can be on your way to building a successful practice group. This is a guide that you can read in hours and not spend several days on. My objective is to keep things simple, use real life experiences, and give you something that you can apply.

There are pointers and tips while performing Qigong – preparing you before your first class, with bonus materials that will make you look like a professional teacher. My goal is to make you look like you have been doing this for a very long time before you start your very first session. You'll be more organized, more prepared, and definitely more confidence than you did before. I am sharing with you my experiences from when I first started teaching, giving you the basics (and some gold nuggets from the pros), so that you can run a thriving group.

Remember, when you reach the top of the mountain, keep climbing!!

Thank you for purchasing this book. I hope it will be very helpful to you and your group(s).

Cheers!!

Jim Cormican

Author and Qigong Practitioner

INTRODUCTION

Welcome to the first ever published practical guide to help you start your own Qigong practice group. Just reading the title "Qigong ~ Mastering Your Own Practice Group" sounds very exciting. Just imagine leading your own Qigong group helping others to learn this wonderful ancient art. This is a great opportunity for you to help guide people in their lives by providing them with simple tools to balance their energy, and remove energy blockages in their body.

To provide such a service in your community, honestly it's going to take some time and effort on your part. It's not going to be magical that one day your group will grow to about 20 people in just a few sessions. If you are patient, you can grow your group to any size you want. It will take some hard work on your part, but I am going to share a secret with you that can make all the difference in the world.... *"Your Heart is the Window to the Journey of your Life."*

Think about that statement and let it sink in. I asked myself a question one day on how I would accomplish starting and running a Qigong practice group. And that profound statement came to me. I don't know where it came from; but it sounded like a pretty good nugget of advice. In reading this statement it tells me if you're going to be successful at what you do, listen to your heart. It's the gateway to your soul, and it should be directing you on your journey through life. I have been following that nugget of advice, and it has taken me on some very interesting journeys.

Since you have an interest in Qigong, your heart has helped you in taking your first steps in learning a wonderful art in not just healing, but learning more about yourself and your surroundings. Since you picked up this book your inner self may be directing you towards starting your own practice group or fine-tuning the current one(s) you have. So go with all your heart. Listen to it. And feel it!

So ask yourself, why did you pick up this book? Are you currently at a Qigong event and having the time of your life? Maybe the title of this book excited you and deep down you wanted to learn how to start your own practice group? Are the things that you have experienced lately telling you that there is more to this? Do you think that starting your own practice group may lead you down a path that will provide you more answers to this mysterious art called Qigong? Is the universe telling you something? Could this be a signpost of things to come?

Remember........picking up this book is just the first step in opening the door. The key to starting and mastering your own practice group.... You have to walk through that door that has opened up for you. It sounds scary at first, but I hope reading this book will empower you to at least try it, and see what opportunities await you on the other side.

So how do you start your own Qigong practice group? How much is involved? Is it complicated? Where do you begin? Can anyone do it?

These are some of top questions asked by people like you who have an interest in starting their own practice group. So how do you start and master your own Qigong sessions? Read on.....

This book is to help you get over the many challenges that instructors and myself have gone through. Think of it as a compilation of the successes from the many mistakes that were made. Then fine-tuned for better results, and sharing those successes with you so that you too can quickly become a professional in facilitating a Qigong practice group.

This is a quick reference guide for those who practice any form of Qigong in a group environment with recurring practice sessions. The information provided is more focused on the people and not the style of Qigong I've learned. Some of my background and experience also comes from the many years of creating, running, and growing Special Interest Groups (SIG) in the business world. I decided to use these skills that I learned in creating social groups and apply it towards my first Qigong practice group since I noticed that there were several similarities between them. I wanted to see what can be used in not just starting a group, but organizing it and providing something tangible so that others can start using this information right away and not end up reinventing the wheel.

And while in the process of doing this, giving you useful information so that you can start applying it right away to start your first group and others if you so desire. This process is sometimes referred to as the cookie-cutter method.

What steps must you take to prepare yourself for such a new journey, a path that you have never walked down before?

The best thing to do is study and learn as much as you can. Visit websites, talk to others, ask questions from the Masters, and get involved. When I was new to Qigong and practicing, I deeply wanted to share with others what I recently learned. You may also feel the same way. You experienced something or noticed others getting results and you wanted to learn as much as you can and teach it to others.

I was a newborn in an old and mysterious world of Qigong, and I knew I had a lot to learn. I decided to get more involved and sign up for classes. When I did, I had the great opportunity to be trained. Later on I found out how to qualify in starting a practice group and I furthered my studies by emerging myself in books and videos on Qigong. After I was trained, the universe moved me away from my family and friends and landed me in Wisconsin.

I ended up with a new job, living in a small town, in a neighborhood of around 30 people or less and surrounded by forest. It was a great place of peace and tranquility, and a lot of wilderness animals to entertain the dog and myself. It was a place of Zen, sharing it with only three chairs and a table – the only furniture I had. This was where this book was first created and the journey began practicing Qigong and running practice groups.

This book was written from my own experience as a Qigong practitioner. The information here was gathered while forming my own Qigong practice groups, and extracted from the many notes I took during the process. While looking back at my entries (during my first year), I spent over 400 hours in one year practicing and I don't think that I have even scratched the surface yet.

With any new routine you start, especially doing it daily, can be a struggle since you have to carve out an hour or so per day to practice. This is a big commitment. I know 400 looks like a large number, but if you do it daily for a year, plus teach classes it starts to add up. It was very difficult in the beginning for me - starting a new routine with a new job, living in another state away from my family, trying to stretch the dollars to support more than one household, and supporting a family member with a severe illness from a distance.......... My world was much different than what I was used to. My surroundings were different, including the culture, cheese curds, the devoted Green Bay Packer fans......so I had to adapt quickly.

Plus, starting my first Qigong Practice Group in an area where no one else was teaching or even heard of Qigong; Alone, I was breaking new ground in an unfamiliar place. So I had to map things out on where to start, who my participants would be, and when should I start it.

With all the craziness in my life, and trying to teach Qigong, it was taking a toll after a while, especially struggling with depression. A voice deep down inside me told me to keep going, that this would all change, and that this is just temporary. After several months of practicing and teaching, I was on the brink of quitting Qigong. I was seeing results, but they were just minor.

I expected big changes, especially practicing daily for many months, but this was not happening. Things started to get frustrating at work also. The work atmosphere had changed, and the morale of the place was plummeting quickly. There were many changes also going on at home.

I realize now, that I brought a different type of energy to the workplace, one with love and compassion for those I worked with, and it was a very strong catalyst that started to shake things up in a very toxic environment. It was complete chaos on a daily basis.

With the many pressures of work and home, I didn't know what to do. I needed something to carry me through these difficult days. Then one day, I received a very different dream in my sleep, it was one of those very powerful dreams that you are very conscious of your surroundings, and it no longer felt like a dream, but it was.

You have this very strong awareness, and you feel you have complete control of your surroundings. Everything feels very real, and events continue going on around you, they feel like they are orchestrated and not important or even influenced by your presence. It's like your dream is playing on without you while you are the observer.

I felt a very strong presence next to me in my dream, and when I tried to look at them, they would not show their face. They would always turn away. They had a conversation with me and I was given some advice. They told me in a very booming voice "The master is within you." This voice was powerful and booming….it shook the world around me. When I awoke, I could still feel their presence around me, and for some time after. I believe that this was a very strong message, so I continued to press on in learning and teaching Qigong.

I don't completely understand the message, but it is not something to think about and try to analyze, it was a message of something that I believe that must be felt deep down inside, but I am sure it will reveal itself to me someday. It was a strong enough message to keep me going for the many months to come. I realized at that point that Qigong had now become a staple of my diet and part of my life. I have worked so hard over the many months and devoted many hours and I know it will pay off in the long run – Physically, Emotionally, Mentally, and Spiritually.

With all the madness around me, I believe practicing Qigong got me through some difficult moments in my life and it was just the beginning of a chapter in my life. Where will it lead? I don't know, but I await patiently for what is to come, and I am very optimistic about the results.

My goal when I first started was to do at least an hour a day, not missing one single day, and keep going no matter what happens. I adopted this rule that Dan Millman wrote in his book *"Everyday Enlightenment: The Twelve Gateways to Personal Growth"*. The rule is, if I miss a day of practicing an exercise, I would start over. If I reach 100, and skip a day, I start back to day one. I thought that this was a good rule to follow, something to help me discipline myself, and continuing the practice of Qigong. I created my own spreadsheets marking the days as they passed (a sample spreadsheet is on our website that companions this book), with what I had completed.

After several months, I noticed I had created a new habit, one that would stick with me for several years. This was my motivation and still is to this day, to check off every day of the accomplishment I had reached. At the point of starting Qigong, I was already following Dan Millman's daily "Peaceful Warrior Workout" (out of his Everyday Enlightenment book) for over 2 years, never missing a single day. So I decided to adopt this rule for practicing Qigong. I would highly recommend his book as part of your own personal growth in Qigong. You can really learn a lot about yourself and get some very useful tips from Dan, which can be applied towards your practice with a life of living Qigong. His book is not on Qigong, but a book, like many of his others, will change your life and inspire you.

Two of his other books that are my favorite and have been very inspirational to me… "Way of the Peaceful Warrior" and "The Journey of Socrates". Read these, and if you enjoy them, add them to your arsenal.

You've read this far and if the idea still appeals to you, let's continue this journey together. On a personal note, between you and me, I would like to thank you for picking up this book. One of the main reasons I sat down and wrote this was to put useful information into your hands. To help guide you in a process that may seem scary at first, since you may feel like you're walking into the unknown alone.

So having a companion can help alleviate some of those fears, and help put the pieces of the puzzle together, and create a picture that will become familiar to you. I am here to help guide you, and remove some of those barriers so you can become successful at starting a group, but remember, along the way your true guides will be love, compassion, and forgiveness. You will be making some mistakes along the way, so don't forget to apply forgiveness, love and compassion towards yourself. Yes, you are that important.

While making mistakes, like many others, don't be embarrassed. Just smile, acknowledge it in the moment, and continue on. Your students will not hold it against you. We are all human after all.

BOOKS PURPOSE

This manual is a guide in helping you facilitate, organize, and teach a Qigong practice group. I am very excited for you since running your own practice group is very exhilarating. Maybe you've started your own practice group, or perhaps you belong to one and wanted to teach a group for yourself. Possibly you watched a DVD and felt deep down inside that your path is to share what you leaned with others, or you just took a class on Qigong, and like me, you were jazzed up and wanted more. Whatever your reasons, you are taking the first steps in sharing what you learned in helping others on their path of change and growth in their lives.

If you want to run your own Qigong practice group, then this is the book for you. I try to keep things very simple with methods and techniques that can be applied with great results. I thought that some type of book was needed to teach others on how to start and improve a Qigong practice group. I searched, but could not find anything out there. Qigong is very new to the United States and throughout other parts of today's world, even though it has been around for thousands of years.

So what do you do when you want to teach a group of people? How do get the word out? After meeting the qualifications in starting a group, what do you do and where do you go? What are the first steps? These were the thoughts that have gone through minds of many people, and starting a group can take a lot of time and great effort. You can end up struggling with it, it can be frustrating at times, and you may decide to hang it up and dissolve the group. You may not be able to find others who can help you, and calling the corporate HQ can also be limiting at times even though they are doing their very best in helping you, but it may not be enough in your circumstance.

So I decided to write this book to share experiences in starting and building a Qigong practice group, and helping with eliminating a lot of the struggles. I have also included many of my documents that I used over the years including a two-hour presentation for those who want to teach people the basics of Qigong as an overview, before people start joining practice groups. I have listed many of the documents that I have created in the back of this book. My website will contain any updates or additions that I have made or been shared by others.

I try to keep things straight to the point and not long winded since I think it is very important that you get your nugget of information and try it right away. The purpose of this book is to also help others who want to start a group, to improve it, and hopefully help those who may be struggling. The information has been tried and tested and I have taken much information from my notes from over the years when I started getting involved with Qigong. I have spent many hours writing down my experiences, noting what works and what doesn't, and making changes to my documents to make improvements.

I hope this information will be very useful to you so you can walk away with some great ideas to help you launch or improve your social group of Qigongers. Please visit our website and share your thoughts with us on how your group is doing and post questions if you need any help.

CHAPTER ONE
The Prep Work

"That Which You Are Seeking is Causing You to Seek"
– Cheri Huber

WHAT WILL YOU NEED?

Starting anything new may take some time to set up. With strong perseverance, and a lot of patience, over time you'll become an expert.

When that very first day arrives when you will be setting up for your practice group, what will you bring? Will you be prepared? Think of it as going on a trip. What do you do to prepare for that destination that will be far from home? What will you need to make it through the day to avoid any headaches? Are you going to need a bag to carry your items in? Do you have a backup plan, like when it may rain on your trip? Would you be ready for any changes?

Expect the unexpected. As you well know, what you envision in your head doesn't manifest in a way that you think it will. You can't prepare for everything in life since it has no instruction manual, plus anything can happen. But you do the best you can and that's what we'll do here. To help you on your trip to your practice group, I have put together a laundry list to prepare you for your session.

Note: Some of the information focuses on the Qigong that I learned, but can be adapted to any style you have learned.

To begin, here is what I recommend before starting your first group:

- **Intro DVD/Video to Qigong:** Depending on the organization that produced the DVD/Video for your training, watch this video over and over again. Take notes, practice it daily and get to know it. Even create some flash cards and quiz yourself on it to help retain the information. Do the exercises out of sequence and see if you can name them. The DVD may also come with a book. Read it from cover to cover several times over and take notes. Build your knowledge of Qigong by practicing it daily. Ask questions if you don't understand something. There are people to help support your efforts in learning Qigong.

- **Find a Practice Group:** I would suggest finding an active group in your area. See how others are doing it. Learn a few pointers from the instructor. Pick their brain on their experiences of teaching a class. Join a class and learn how the instructor interacts with their students. See how long the class is. Talk with those who attend and get their feedback before and after class. What is it that they like, or dislike? How long have they been attending? If there is no practice group in your area, watch the Qigong DVD/Video and start practicing with that.
- **This Book and our Website:** Read this book from cover to cover, mark it up with your notes, and also go through our website. The website will contain very useful information and customizable documentation along with a two hour presentation that can be edited and used for teaching an overview class. There will also be handouts for your students, fliers to use for marketing, business card templates, waivers, and other documents to help you get started before your first day of class.
- **Pressure Points:** I am not endorsing or recommending anyone's book here, but there are some great self-healing manuals by some of the great Qigong Masters that are out there. Just search online or talk to another practice group leader. Use this as a bonus for you students. Pick out a healing method and teach it before the end of class. I use one self-healing technique per Qigong practice session, and there are plenty in some of these books for one year if you are doing just a weekly session.
- **Practice 100 days Straight:** Before starting my practice group, I did Qigong daily, and sometimes twice daily. Get familiar with the exercises. For 100 days, I got to know each exercise, what order to do it in, their names, how long it took to complete, and along the way I made a lot of mistakes and got these out of the way before teaching my first class. This was very helpful in the learning process. I would question myself during the exercises to get a better understanding of what the movements are doing. I would ask myself, "What is the meaning behind this particular exercise? What does it do for my body?" Asking many questions and researching it will help you find your answers, ones that your students may also ask you one day since you shared the same curiosity.

- **Storage for Your Belongings:** Find yourself a backpack, duffle bag, or tote bag, something to carry your Qigong stuff (like handouts, maybe speakers for playing music, books for reference, etc.). You will be using this to teach your class. It's like a portable filing cabinet for your signup sheets, handouts, and other things you can think of that you would be using in class.
- **MP3 Player:** I use a smart phone during my sessions. I plug it into my docking station that has speakers. I will use it for meditation or music during practice. You can download streaming music apps to your smartphone or MP3 player to use in class. Try to avoid the ones that do advertising if you decide to use their service for background music.

Here is my Gear for Playing Music and Meditation. I use my Smartphone, Speakers, and a Remote Control to Regulate the Volume, Pause, or Shut it off From a Distance. It has Been Very Useful for Many of my Practice Sessions.

You may have to pay a subscription, but as long as you don't get advertising announced over your speakers while you're teaching, you should be ok. Within that app, you can do a search for Yoga music, Dao, Tao, Reiki music, Zen, meditation, spirit, music of India, etc. and add it into your collection. You should be able to create your own stations and play a variety of soft meditative music, or find a CD that uses a self-guided meditation.

Don't forget to put your phone in airplane mode so you won't receive calls, or text messages during your session. I use to get calendar alerts during my session, so I also took care of this, especially if I use my phone for presentations. My personal life kept popping up on the screen (reminder – pick up groceries after class, walk the dog, birthday announcements, etc.) and text messages from family members. Yep, it could be embarrassing and entertaining to your audience. So make sure that these are shut off.

PRACTICE WHAT YOU PREACH

I am a firm believer if that if you're going to teach something, you should practice it yourself before sharing it with others. There are so many who spread their words of wisdom, but have had no experience in what they are talking about. What's important is not spew things out to people if you really don't know it. It may sound really good, but if the information is incorrect, things will get complicated later. Learn how to do it first, and get some experience around it. Ask questions yourself if you don't know.

Practice and learn, you'll get good at what you do and it will reflect in how you teach. Doing so will also build a lot of trust and confidence with those you work with. If you're also going to preach some sort of wisdom to your audience on Qigong, I would hope that you're following your own advice. Let me give an example.

I've attended many seminars over the years while I was a business owner, made many connections, and have become good friends with several other business owners. They would share their advice with the audience, and present their great ideas to help others become successful. Some of the advice was so simple and basic (sort of common sense) to follow that it could make their business grow and increase revenue for their attendees. I also noticed that some of these owners struggled and struggled with their own business. They doled out some really awesome information, but in the end, they were not practicing their own advice. They were so tied up in trying to grow their own business, they too forgot the basics for themselves. I have seen too many of these people fail at what they do, and continue to struggle over and over again because they didn't listen to themselves.

If you're going to teach a group of people on how to do Qigong, you're going to have to immerse yourself in it. Be a part of it, incorporate it into your daily routine and your life. This is how you'll become very skillful in this practice and get much better at teaching it to others because you're sharing your experience. You're practicing what you preach, and at the same time, becoming an expert in what you do. Follow your own advice especially when given to others. Keep to the basics and you will grow, become successful at what you do, and also see your group mirror your accomplishments.

DIFFERENT EXPERIENCES

As a practitioner, you are going to have different sensations and experiences than others in your group. Just keep this in mind. You can share your experience with others, but don't set the expectation that they will experience the same results as you. Everyone is different in how their body works with energy. We are all unique in who we are and with that, experiences are also going to be unique as well. You will also have people who will have no experiences at all, which is okay. Explain this to the group as well so people aren't looking for the same similarities as you and get lost and lose interest or caught up in something that may never happen. If they think they should have one and don't, they will be discouraged and will feel like they are not part of something special, drop out, and have a bad experience with Qigong.

Have this conversation before starting your first class. You can also do this during the Qigong Overview presentation if you decide to do one. There is a section in the power point presentation (downloadable from our website) that lists the types of experiences that people may have, and also mention that people may not have any experience at all.

Energy has intelligence behind it and will go where it is needed. There are some who do healing on themselves and never feel anything (like heat, cold, tingling sensations, etc.), but the healing energy vibration they give to others can be felt. I have talked to others who have experienced this and even though they do get results with themselves, they continue to look for something. Not to worry, energy consists of frequencies/vibrations, and just imagine that the energy that you are receiving is at the same frequency/vibration as your body. Since they are the same, you may not feel anything. So just think of it that you are in tune with yourself. Everyone is going to be different, so don't go looking for something. The universe will provide and it is usually not what you expect.

When I was doing a healing session on an individual during a group meditation, we ran out of time and another scheduled group had just arrived for their stretching session given by another instructor. I told the individual that I was sorry that we ran out of time and didn't get to work on her. She said that while I was sending energy to the person next to her, she felt it. To her it came as a slight breeze, and it was warming her. I was curious since I didn't feel any breeze, and we were in a closed room, and I did not see any ventilation near us. I did not share this same experience as she did, nor the person I was working with. So remember, everyone is going to have different experiences, and sometimes similar ones.

YOUR 100 DAY SELF-PRACTICE

Before I started my first practice session, I did a 100 day self-practice of doing Qigong and a meditation. Before you begin teaching your first class, set out and do the 100 straight days of Qigong. Get to know and gain the experience in what you'll be teaching to others. By doing so, this will help you in preparing before your first session with your students. It will take you that long to learn the exercises, organize your thoughts, and put yourself into the shoes of those who would be in your practice group. When I practiced during the first 100 days, I read anything I could on the style of Qigong I learned; I took the necessary classes, organized my notes and was even part of a weekly and monthly group sessions to learn from other Qigong practitioners.

This also gave me the time to write down my thoughts, research, contact the Headquarters where I learned Qigong to get answers to my questions, and chat with other instructors. I also purchased the DVDs that was offered, read the books that came with it several times, which helped me better understand the movements and learn more about Qigong.

Note: *It is very important that when you are seeking answers, ask the organization that taught you (or the people within). If there is a lack of support, I would suggest looking for another group that will be there for you. You are investing your time and hard earned money into something that you should get support and if it's not available, there is no way for you to support those you teach or advance yourself. If this is the case, you may have to look deep inside yourself and make that hard decision to consider looking elsewhere.*

You want to do your research while you are practicing, this will help build up your confidence and improve your knowledge before you teach. During my studies, I also noted key words (the language used in Qigong) so that I communicated the correct messages to my group. Like any environment you work in, there is a lingo associated with that particular profession and learning the language/glossary will help further yourself and your students. It will also help those who want to advance to higher levels in Qigong, so they don't end up struggling because they learned the incorrect words and their meanings.

If you use a different lingo other than the one taught to you in Qigong, they will end up confused with information that is different than their Qigong training offered by certified instructors. Keep it simple and use common language that was taught to you when you went through the training. If you are uncertain with something, please contact those who trained you. They will be very happy to assist and help you with something you don't understand.

I AM NOT READY TO TEACH

You've done 100 days straight of Qigong and meditation, you've read the books over and over, took a lot of notes, but you feel that you're quite not ready yet. So now what? That's perfectly okay. Not all of us can learn something and jump right in, especially teaching it right away. We all have different styles and different times when we feel when we are ready. If it is the fear of teaching in front of a group of strangers, I can completely understand.

When I started doing presentations in front of an audience of people I was a natural and could present in front of a crowd of 50 to a couple of hundred people - no problem. But when it came down to a small group, a strange fear came over me. I had problems presenting and trouble getting the right words to form and I felt I was doing a real miserable job in not delivering my message as clear as I wanted to. I could not understand why I had such difficulties. How can I present in front of hundreds but not to a handful of people. I was baffled, I was consumed with some sort of nervousness, and ended up heated and sweaty when I was done. I should have felt comfortable during my presentation, but felt sick and full of fear.

I brought this problem to a friend of mine who was a professional public speaker and I was stumped as to why I got so nervous in front of a small crowd of people. I was told that when I am in front of a large audience, there is no single person I focus on, it's just a sea of bobbing heads, and no real identity associated with them. But when I am in front of just a few people, I felt that there was a trust-relationship since it is more of a one-on-one, and that it was more on a personal level. Like having a face to the name. This made perfect sense to me and my nervousness went away after a while.

If you think you'll be nervous, don't worry. Once you start getting into the groove of things, it'll pass. To get yourself going, I would highly recommend that you put pen to paper and start writing out a schedule. Get yourself motivated on what day you will begin your first class, and beyond. Lock yourself in on a date and time you will start your first class. Give yourself an agenda of what you will be teaching in class. Visualize on how you will do it. Practice in an empty room if necessary to familiarize yourself in how you will teach it.

Once you get people attending and you feel like you are still not ready, grab your Qigong DVD and play it for your group (some Qigong organizations have a DVD to learn from). Have that person in the video lead your group for you until you feel you are up to speed and ready to teach. Just continue using the DVD until you get to the point where you feel comfortable. After doing a few sessions, you may surprise yourself and start taking over. Take a leap of faith and guess what? You'll amaze yourself. You'll make mistakes along the way (we all do) while not using the DVD, but remember, that's okay.

We've all done it. Just do your very best. I myself have made plenty of mistakes. I have skipped one of steps in one of the Qigong exercises and several times I have forgotten my left from my right when starting an exercise. I have also found myself repeating the same side. So, is it okay to make mistakes? Absolutely, you have everyone's blessing, including your students.

I have even forgotten what the next step was in the exercise. Did I panic? Sure did, but I progressed and moved onto the next step. About 99% of the time, your students will not notice, they are new to Qigong. I'll bet any one of your Qigong Masters were also nervous and made several mistakes when they taught their first class. Remember, your students are also there to support you, and they want to make you successful in what you do, plus you can't forget that the universe and all its energy is in your corner. With all that, you have a really good chance of being an excellent instructor, even if you don't think so in the very beginning. After a while you will start to surprise and amaze yourself.

If you make a mistake, keep going. You will take a mental note of it, beat yourself up over it in your mind. Remember it the next time and learn from your mistakes. So in other words, it is okay to make mistakes. I find myself an hour later thinking, "Oh my, I just remember I forget a step in my teachings", or it comes to me while meditating the very next day. Don't let it get you down. We all learn from our mistakes, so you will make them along the way, guaranteed. Correct them the next time around. Even doing the exercises a hundred times in a row, I sometimes find myself goofing. I have also asked others who teach and they also do the same. Why? We are all human and allowed to make mistakes.

Whatever you decide to do in your delivery method of teaching, remember everyone is learning and experiencing the wonders of Qigong.

100 DAY QIGONG – STARTING THE HABIT

Before you take the task on in teaching others, do Qigong for 100 day challenge along with the meditation (if one was provided). Create a daily habit of practicing every day. I have a strict rule to keep me practicing. I will do the exercises daily, keep track of it, and number the days. If I miss a day, I start all over by removing my log and throwing it in the trash. I pull out another spreadsheet and start from day one again. So far I have been doing pretty well. I have so far while writing this book completed 915 days straight in practicing Qigong without missing one single day.

There are several reason why I do this is, but the results are a daily discipline through a routine I stick with. Believe me, there are days I don't feel like getting out of bed, but I do. I have to. It has become a part of my lifestyle now.

I just think about throwing that piece of paper with all my hard work into the trash receptacle. That's a visual that keeps me going in the morning and a reality that I don't want to experience. Goal setting is very important in helping you make accomplishments. By practicing frequently, you are living by example. If you want to seriously train people on the art of Qigong, you have to live, breath, and experience it. Not just do it. This will help you in teaching your class, build confidence in yourself in what you teach, and open up other opportunities.

Set some kind of goal. If it's Qigong daily, every other day, or whatever... Stick with it after you complete your 100 days. I do it daily, and have been for several years. It's really hard, especially when routines start to change.

While doing your 100 day stint, just imagine yourself surrounded by your students and you are giving direction. See yourself doing the moves, speaking out loud on the benefits of Qigong, showing how slow a movement should go, how many repetitions, and so forth. Practicing this daily will get you in the mindset and help build your confidence in teaching to an audience. Speak out loud while you do this. Practice your tone, your pitch, and just visually imagine filling your living room with students as you teach.

I have included on the website that compliments this book, an editable spreadsheet for your Qigong exercises that can be used to keep track of your progress. It is a great way to build a repetition that will maintain a retention, and help form a new daily habit. I give it to those students who want to practice daily and keep track of how they are doing.

NOTE: When I started doing the 100 days of Qigong, including a meditation that I would teach in class, I started out fine. But after a while I was getting sleepy during the meditation and lost my place several times. I tried different things to prevent this, but was not getting results. I ended up doing my meditation first, then doing the Qigong exercises. When I did my exercises first, my body became very relaxed, then when I was done I would go into the meditation. At times I was way too relaxed and caught myself dozing off. So if you end up in the same situation, try reversing the process and do your meditation first. See if this makes a difference. Try experimenting to see what works best for you.

I also tried different positions, like laying down (this at times I would catch myself snoring again), different types of chairs with different backs, sitting up against walls, and even sitting up in bed. If you do the meditation in a place that you usually sleep in (like your bed), this can signal the mind and body that it's time to sleep. It's like a habit that has already been formed and if you try to break this, you may end up having problems sleeping in bed at night.

So avoid anything that can trigger the mind and body thinking that it's sleep time. Make sure you find something that is comfortable for you, but not too comfortable. I use a wooden chair, which is not uncomfortable, but not too comfortable. Also avoid those big lazy boy chairs (American style chairs that can recline and can be wonderfully comfortable that you can even sleep in) for meditation. It's like sleeping in the hands of the Universe, very peaceful with a whole lot of love.

STRUCTURE & DISCIPLINE

As you grow in learning and teaching Qigong, you will notice some disciplines growing within yourself. For example, you may notice that you are setting expectations with yourself on improving your class, like arriving early before your students, you may find yourself becoming more organized, or you start practicing Qigong daily at 3 am. You may also notice that you start your class on time and end on time. Or life in general, you notice changes about yourself, changes in areas that others are also noticing about you.

Having some sort of structure around your practice group is important. An example would be to arrive to class at least 15 minutes early. As a student, it is important that their instructor is punctual and not chronically late. Being tardy several times for your own class speaks volume to your students of having little discipline or respect. Let your students know ahead of time that showing up late would impact the class and the enjoyment of those who attend. Tell them that it is very much appreciated by all when arriving on time. If they know they will be late, they can also make the next session. They are always welcomed.

You may all be meditating and a door slams, or there is shuffling going on, or whispers as someone walks in late. If you set this expectation of arriving a little earlier before class starts, your students will deeply respect you because this shows that you respect them and value their time. They are there to learn and have taken time from their busy lives to be with you and the group. Some of you I have spoken to allow students to be late, and this is due to the establishment that you teach at.

They have rules set in place to allow this to happen for

purposes that work best for them and their participants, for example - crisis centers, rehabs, hospitals, hospices, etc. Respect your student's time and get them out on time. Don't let it go into overtime. Most people in your class are on a schedule and have to be somewhere after class - like picking up their kids, meeting their significant other, going to work, a doctor appointment, etc.

When I have seen people show up late, this is distracting, annoying, and your students may think this person does not respect you as a teacher. Put a sign on the door (sign provided on our website), that tells them that the class has started and that you will see them at the next practice. If you allow people to just come around at any time, you have lost control of the group, you may lose respect from others, and you will also notice a decline in attendance.

Let people know the guidelines, and if they can't be followed, you can politely ask them to find another group. People do talk after the practice and if they don't like something, they will let others know and if people aren't happy, the next thing you know, you have no one showing up. Try to keep a pulse of what's going on. Engage with them, maybe do a survey, or just talk with them.

Set the tone, tell them you respect their time, and you will have a great group of people who will be attending for years.

WHEN TO PRACTICE BY YOURSELF

For me, the best time starts around 3:30 am (this is due to my current schedule at the time). Too early you think? You're not an early bird?

Getting up early is not favorable amongst most people, and it can be a big change in someone's life, but the purpose of this topic is to find what best fits for you when you chose to practice Qigong. It could be at noon, late morning, or in the evening. Getting up very early is the lifestyle I have chosen which fits into my daily routine, but yours will be totally different from mine. I just wanted to share with you what I do so it can give you some ideas that you may try to adapt for yourself. I have a good reason for getting up very early, I try to get up before anyone else is awake, plus it is the perfect time to be alone, to take notes, to practice and not be bothered by the starting of the day's activities. When 6 am starts rolling around, most people are up and the chaos begins.

I don't remember how many times that I have gotten that early call when I have to drop everything and focus on the problem at hand, and the rest of my day is shot and I am trying to find the time to practice. "If I only should have gotten up earlier", is the conversation that starts in my mind over and over again as if it is trying to resolve the problem of how to do it better the next time. You feel like your whole day and your routine is ruined, and you try your best to get it back on track, but your day is already in motion. You're hitting the ground running not knowing where your feet are taking you, and it can be late in the evening before you can start practicing, trying to complete your scheduled routine for the day.

Many of us have busy lifestyles, we feel like we don't have enough time in the day. This has happened to me a few times, so I decided, to go to bed early (around 8 – 9 pm), and get up early. You're probably thinking about that new television show that comes on at 9 pm and you don't want to miss it. There's plenty of technology in the world to record it and watch it at a later date. I have eliminated much of my television watching to give myself some extra time for myself and my family.

After a routine of doing this for several months, I have created a healthy habit, get plenty of rest, and I feel less stress in my life. I feel that I am at the helm again, navigating my own ship and it feels like it's on course.

If you have children, and or married, your time really gets absorbed by the needs of others. You are juggling different schedules, like trying to get kids off to school, getting breakfast ready for the family, preparing for work, and end up fighting traffic trying to get to your next destination. It becomes utter chaos. So what do you do with all this craziness? Find yourself a quiet place, away from the family, and practice.

I put a sign on my door (the one I use for my practice groups – found on the website) telling anyone who is walking by to not disturb me. Sometimes it works, depending on the age of the child. You may have to have a conversation with your family asking not to be disturbed while you are practicing and have others support you by herding the little ones away from your door while the sign is hanging.

So if your family gets up around a particular time, give yourself about 1- 2 hours beforehand. This will give you a little buffer of time when you get out of bed, get dressed, brush your teeth, set up you practice area, and go to your happy place. Once you fine-tune your time, you may find yourself incorporating some additional meditation time.   When people in my family get up a little earlier than usual, I can hear them in the kitchen, walking the hallways, turning on the TV, etc. I would wear headphones or ear plugs, so I am not disturbed. Very helpful when you think you're running behind schedule and you go a few minutes over your set time.

CHAPTER TWO
Building Your Group

*"If You Have no Obstacles in Your Own Mind,
Then Outer Obstacles will not Hinder You or
Cause You Worry"*
- Hsuan Hua

WHERE DO YOU START?

Before you begin teaching a class to others, I would recommend that you learn Qigong in-depth. What I mean by in-depth is that you integrate it into your life by practicing all the time. Eat, sleep, and drink Qigong. Put forth that extra effort in studying and understanding; make the commitment of doing Qigong every day for over 3 months (or longer).

If you can do 200 days, or 300, that's awesome! You will start noticing your improvement in performing and your confidence increasing as you practice Qigong. After a while, you'll become proficient in the exercises, know the name of each one, and can do all the exercises from start to finish. After a while when you know the names, start incorporating the descriptions into your routine of knowing what each exercise does. For example, when you are doing the basic Qigong stance, imagine you have students in front of you and say what each exercise does. "This exercise is called, balancing Yin and Yang. What this does is re-balance the energy in your body". Memorize these because you will be able to distinguish what each one does and the benefits that are associated with them.

Also continue your studies by visiting that particular Qigong website and read their articles, ask questions from their Headquarters, watch some videos, sign up for their newsletter, visit other websites of those who also teach Qigong. There is a lot of information available to you. So during the exercises, what you've learned, can also be applied while you are practicing with your group.

Imagining students in front of you when you practice and making mistakes then, will really pay off when you teach your own group.

So practice, practice, practice, and study, study, study!

MANAGING YOUR TIME

At times you will have to adjust your exercises to respect the time of your students. Time is a factor and everyone is on a schedule, so you want to begin and end your class timely. Let's say that you are done with your exercises but have more time on the clock, what do you do? For example, you have an extra 5-7 minutes. I would extend the meditation 5 - 7 minutes to balance out the time. If you're behind, shorten the length of one or two in your time schedule of the exercises so you can complete all the exercises.

For example, you can decrease the meditation time, or decrease the time in one of your exercises. Once you start practicing Qigong frequently, you will notice that you are pretty close to finishing at a specific time. You may take 45 minutes to do your exercises, so add 10 minutes of meditation and a Q&A at the end, or teach one healing technique out of a self-healing book.

On the website I have also included a checklist that is adaptable for any self-healing technique. This is helpful so you don't repeat the same technique during the year for your practice group. It is also very helpful in organizing when you are doing more than one practice group. You will need to find a self-help healing book (using pressure points for pain management and healing for example) learn techniques from it, and teach them to your group. It adds a lot of value to your sessions.

For every overview class (the class where I introduce Qigong), I teach the same technique. Like how to stop a bloody nose. This means you don't have to figure out what you already taught in the overview and duplicate it in your regular sessions. Just pick one thing for the Qigong overview presentation, always use it, and then use the self-healing checklist for your regular practice group. This way you will avoid duplication and confusion.

STARTING YOUR GROUP - PREPARATION

Starting a group is going to be difficult at first. So what do you do? Where do you find those people with the same interest? How do you retain them? When is the best time to schedule?

Where's the location you will be practicing? These and many other questions will run through your head. It's not going to be easy at first. You must have really good organizational skills, people skills, and of course being comfortable in leading a group of people.

When you first glanced at the title of this book, many ideas came to mind. One of them might be the desire to share and teach Qigong to others.

If you lack some of the skills mentioned above, have someone help you that have those strengths. Have them put together those areas in which you need help, and then go into action. All the areas that you struggle with will be done for you. Skills can be developed over time; you just have to have the desire to do it. It's like learning anything. Practice, Practice, Practice!! Once you strengthen those areas, you can be completely on your own.

When I first started my group (it was at the place where I was employed), I thought to myself, starting a practice group at work would be no problem. I was already surrounded by many people and we all worked for the same company. Depending on the size of the company you work for (there were several hundred at my location), it may not work the way you think it will. Most people will have no idea what Qigong is; especially knowing how to say it when they read it. They don't know what you know, so education is key here, especially on delivering the message to your audience.

When talking to people, use key words that they understand. If you talk about Qi/Chi, chakras, third eye, dantians, life force, energy healing.... Some people will just give you that blank stare or think you need to be admitted to the hospital. My position at the company was very new. I came from the outside and knew no one at first and I was starting fresh, with no familiar faces. I was fortunate to overhear a conversation one day about energy healing from coworkers, so I decided to approach them and listen.

I told them that I was forming a weekly Qigong practice group (also explained to them what it was), and that I would give them a two hour overview on the subject. If they continued to have an interest after my mini-presentation, they could join the group I was forming. So I reserved a conference room and sent invitations to join me. They liked what they experienced during the presentation, and they became my first Qigong practice group. It was a small weekly group, and sometimes I would get about 1 to 3 people, but it was a lot of fun and well worth it.

Don't be disappointed in the size of the group, it's all about quality and not quantity. Once you get a few people attending, they will tell their friends and coworkers and help you grow your group. You need a lot of patience in the beginning. It can be a rough ride, but hang in there. It will grow over a period of time, and remember, be careful what you wish for. If you start asking the universe to send a whole band of people, you may turn out to have a very large group that you may not be able to handle. Can you organize a group of 30, 40, or 50 people? Think about it. What about the space you are in, will it accommodate that many people? Will you have that many chairs?

So make your preparations before you jump in with both feet. Take a good look around and figure out if the place you want to teach is the best place for you and your attendees. Will it be at night? Is there adequate lighting for people to see their vehicles and other people? Is it a safe place for your audience? Have you figured out a time to meet? Just start out with the basics and build upon that foundation you are creating. Don't worry if things start out slow, that's ok. If it takes longer than a month, reevaluate your situation and see where the weak link in the chain is and see if you can repair it.

Once you commit, you must stay with it, and be prepared. I have seen people who would put the word out on a get together, when they are not prepared or ready. The date they advertised gets cancelled at the last moment. Those who would be attending are disappointed. This also doesn't look good if this happens several times. Word will spread about frequent cancellation and by the time you do commit, you may not have anyone showing up. You also want to be all set up and ready to go before your session starts - every time.

HOW MANY GROUPS SHOULD I FACILITATE?

There is so much you can do, but you may also have limited time. I know you have a lot of passion in doing this, but I would suggest just starting out with one group and build it over time. Do this for several months to get comfortable with it, learn from the group, and learn from your mistakes, and when you feel the time is right, start another one. For me, one is good enough. I have other commitments and just doing one fills my schedule. You may have plenty of time, and maybe you want to do one at work and another across town with a senior citizen group. That's great! Just don't overdo it, you may lose quality if you have too many groups, and if your schedule gets too busy, you may have to drop a group or two.

So just build one, stick to it, see if you can grow it to the size that you want, and then decide whether or not you want to expand and start another group. Just keep in the back of your mind how much time and effort it will take you to run two groups during the week, especially if you are building one or both at the same time. My recommendation is to focus on one, doing it for a year or two, and see if having a second group makes sense. There are life changes that can impact juggling two groups, especially if you start a new job and it doesn't give you time to focus on your groups, since you have to drive across town, or you have a schedule that would overlap your groups meeting time.

WHAT TO CHARGE

Once you obtain your certification and are able to charge for teaching Qigong, you may have an interest in creating a supplemental income. You're not going to get rich teaching Qigong, but at least you will be able to recoup for all the training you had to pay for. Charging a fee is up to you. There are classes on Yoga, Tai-chi, Qigong, etc., and for some, there is a price tag associated with learning these arts. You will discover that there are those who charge, and have a deep passion for teaching, and you will meet others who have a passion for just the money.

When this happens the purpose and the reason behind that particular art gets lost. If you do decide to charge, keep the purity of Qigong and don't turn it into a machine to just make money, do it from the heart and soul. Do it for yourself, but also do it for others.

A yoga instructor who was teaching a class that I was in shared her story on how she was very upset with the way yoga is being portrayed here in the US. She feels that such a beautiful thing is moving in a different direction than where yoga should be going, that some instructors are trying to turn it into a money making machine, and straying away from its deep rooted purpose in life. Similar to some of those dojos that you find where you can obtain a black belt in less than two years, but in reality it takes years of practice, discipline, and maturity to reach a level of competency to obtain the level of a black belt.

Taking shortcuts in a special art could become harmful to people if taught incorrectly, providing little experience and knowhow, along with losing its essence. Are the special arts we are receiving from other countries, the ones that have been around for hundreds or even thousands of years, slowly losing true meaning and becoming commercialized in the US and other countries? Are people getting certified too quickly and the quality declining? Folks, let's keep Qigong as pure as possible and not turn it into some sort of commercialized franchise. Let's try and keep the integrity and originality as close as possible like it was thousands of years ago.

Continue to work together in maintaining the quality, keep our focus on helping others heal themselves, and let's not lose sight of it's true essence and meaning, that which has been passed down from generation to generation to you. Keep it pure for the next hundreds or thousands of years so students can benefit from its true essence. Making money is okay, and there is nothing wrong with it. If you make a million, awesome, but the money is not the main mission here. It is to share what we've learned and pass it along to those people who have devoted their time to learn something to help improve their lives.

We have learned something that was carefully guarded for a long time and has now become available to all. Respect it since those from the many generations before you have worked hard to keep it alive, and we are very lucky that much of the knowledge has survived time and has not been lost. It has miraculously ended up in your grasp. This rare opportunity is now with you and you are now part of that long line of people throughout time that have taken the responsibility to preserve and continue the lineage for many generations to come. Qigong has found you and it is a very big deal. It should be honored and not taken for granted.

Since we all live in different places around the world, are part of different cultures, and different economies, what should you charge in the area where you live? Pricing is going to be different throughout the world, so start locally and not globally for what you should charge. Every location is going to be different in what will be charged and it is going to reflect on the type of people who will be attending.

Different social classes will be comfortable with a particular rate since this is what's affordable to them. For example, if you are going to teach in an area that is low income, keep your rate at a level that is not hard on the pocket book. You want people to experience the wonderful world of Qigong, not create a great barrier that would prevent them from attending. Qigong is for everyone and is not focused on a particular class of people. Keep it at a rate that people can continue to attend.

Where should you start in determining your rate? Get a feel for your audience, find out what others are charging for Qigong, Tai Chi, Yoga, etc., in your area. Then offer something competitive to spark some interest. Play around with it to see what people will pay. Try calling around to other places that teach Qigong or Tai Chi and see what they are charging. Ask them questions about what class is popular and why. How long have they been around and ask them what their secret of success is. They may open up and share it with you. See if they ever offer any specials and try adapting or modifying to see if it works for your audience.

There are some health places (gymnasiums, health clubs, spas, etc.) that will let you teach in their facility, but they may want to make money off of your services. You can negotiate with them or they may already have a structured fee in place. They will most likely be advertising for you and providing the space free of charge, so this will save you money. Every business is going to be different.

Once in a while, offer specials to build your group. It could be at a reduced rate, or if you have additional workshops or classes on Qigong, you can provide it free of charge to get people interested. Maybe a package deal with joining your group (practice group and workshops). Get creative in this area.

Once you have settled on your price (remember you may have some additional costs involved), make sure you are making a profit after all the expenses - unless you want to be non-profit (pay out of your own pocket). Don't put yourself in the hole and pay for expenses that you shouldn't be covering. Adjust your rate to cover costs. If it is too high and not unaffordable for people to attend, find a different venue and a different way of doing things. You may have to experiment in this area.

SCHEDULING

So when is the best time to teach a Qigong practice group? The reality of it all is that it needs to start with your schedule. When are you available? Some people reverse it and think of when is the best time for the people. Honestly, that's impossible. Everyone has different schedules. Depending on your culture, picking a day could have an impact where no one is showing up, or just the opposite. Some of us have different holidays and religious days that are celebrated.

Here in the United States, I don't have a regular practice group on a Monday or Friday. Many of our US holidays falls on a Monday. Fridays are at the end of the work week and not many people will want to spend the time doing Qigong with a group since most are celebrating the end of the week, plus it may be a payday and this creates an additional feeling of going out and rewarding oneself for working hard. Most will be needing a little downtime to decompress from a stressful week.

Remember, some people have commitments during the week. You have to consider children and school. Some parents have to go pick up their children. I have one student that is devoted to the practice group, but needs to leave 15 minutes early to pick up her child. That's okay. It doesn't disturb the class, and she is learning Qigong. But she feels like she can't devote her entire time and feels rushed to leave since she has a busy schedule. Others may have religious events to go to after work, maybe another job, a sports event, but just pick what works best for you. But keep some of this in the back of your mind. What day of the week will produce the most attendees that fits in your schedule?

Your best bet, depending on your culture and how things are celebrated, I pick either Tuesday, Wednesday, or Thursday. I haven't done a group yet on Saturday, but you may have those who have an open schedule and wouldn't mind attending. Sunday is usually a day for most family gatherings. You may have a very small audience or none at all.

So find one of those days that fits your schedule. Sit down with a calendar and go through it to determine a good day during the week for you. One of my groups this year lands on a day that has 2 holidays in a row, plus a day of celebration where most people go on vacation the day before. So within 30 days, my weekly class has 2 days where no one would show up, and one that you may or may not have anyone attend. Fortunately, this won't happen for another 7 years. My schedule is very busy and the only time I have is on a Wednesday, right after work from 5:15 – 6:15 pm. At the time of writing on this topic, I teach at the company I work at and this works best for me.

HOW LONG SHOULD CLASS BE?

How long do you think it should be? How much time can you spare? Will your attendees have that amount of time to devote? Class length is going to be primarily up to you since you know your schedule and availability.

Some groups are about an hour to an hour and a half long on average.

Once you have been practicing for a while, how long does it take you to complete the exercises? Does it take you 45 minutes, an hour or more? Take that time and create your practice session.

Then if you feel like adding anything additional, do it and then determine how long it takes.

Before I begin my daily practice, I look at the clock and take note of when I start and when I finish, I also gauge myself in how long it takes to do each exercise. Over time, I noticed I finished around the same time and I use this in my practice group. If it is too long, minimize some of it, so it fits into your practice group time. I may look at the clock 3 times during the period I am teaching. I find myself doing 45- 50 minutes of exercises. Then I dedicate 10 minutes in meditation and what time is left over I go through a Q&A and teach the group a new self-healing technique out of a self-healing book.

You may decide to have your practice group for 1.5 hours. You can do the exercises for about 55 minutes, then do the meditation (on CD or MP3). I have included an outline form on the website for this book, which you can use to keep track of what you teach out of a self-healing book. It makes for a good record of what was taught and what will be available for the next sessions.

VENUE

You may not think it, but having the right place to have your practice group can make it or break it. I have had some experience in this area and having a location that is not convenient for others could end up with no shows. It's like running a business and trying to attract customers. When Mel Brooks said "Location, Location, Location" in Blazing Saddles, he wasn't kidding. How many businesses go under if they can't be seen, or they're hard to get to?

People are looking for a place that will accommodate them. For example, when I used to do events at different locations, one of the young ladies told me that she really appreciated coming to the event in the evening because the parking lot was very well lit. Dark parking lots can be scary for some folks. That was something I never thought of. Distance is also important to people. Considering your location; is it across town, and will take 30 or more minutes to get to? How's the traffic on the way there?

Is it always busy? Is there only one highway to get there, or multiple routes in case one is backed up during the day and an alternate route can be chosen?

VENUE CHECKLIST

How convenient is your location for your group?

Here are some questions to ask yourself.............

- Is there ample parking?
- Do people have to pay for parking?
- Are there parking meters? If so, are they free after a certain time of day?
- If it's in a building, is it easy for people to find inside? Do you have enough signage to guide people through the building? Are you allowed to put up signage?
- What time of day do you offer your class? Would it be during heavy traffic times and time consuming for those coming to your venue?
- Is it real easy to find, or confusing since all the buildings look the same and sign posts are difficult to read or find?
- Can people find the address easily?
- Does your GPS take you to this location, or somewhere down the street, or not able to find it at all?
- Is it on Google maps or MapQuest so people can find it on the Internet?
- Does the venue have working bathrooms? Are they easy to find?
- Is it a high security place where your attendees have to go through security? Will someone be there to greet them and show them where to go? Do they need a visitor badge? You may have to provide a list of attendees to security ahead of time (I've had to do that in the past).
- Does your venue have chairs for those to meditate, for those people who can't stand for periods of time?
- Is it a quiet location? Will there be a lot of noise or traffic in the hallways?
- How many people can fit in the room?

- Is there a projector that you can use to show videos, or Internet access where you can show a video on the web about the effects of Qigong? Maybe a snippet on meditation? Having all this is not a necessity, unless you think you need it to do presentations.
- Is there an area where people can sign in?

Use this as a starter checklist for yourself in determining if a particular location you are looking at will fit your needs. Make sure what you choose will be convenient for your audience and you. If it doesn't feel right, don't go with it. It may have the perfect location, a lighted parking lot, and a great size room with a big screen projector, but down the hallway is a hammer testing facility and all you can hear are hammers banging all the time during your session.

LIMITATIONS WITH YOUR VENUE

You may have an instance where you are limited in what you can do with your group due to the room you will be practicing in.

For example, let's say that you are told that you can no longer have your practice group at the current location where you are. You now have to find a new location. Your next venue may end up with a room that does not have any chairs. Maybe the room is too small. Or it's dark and dank and not really healthy to practice in. So what do you do? At this point, you'll have to put your thinking cap on and be creative with what has been given to you, or find another location.

I too have had these types of instances when looking for a location. Let's say you have a room but it does not have any chairs. The place is a dance studio with very beautiful wooden floors and chairs are not allowed since they could scratch the woodwork. You'll have to use your imagination. What would you do? Do you eliminate the meditation; does your audience need chairs? Is it becoming too challenging? Do you bring in some mats or your own chairs? This all depends on the group you will be teaching to, their challenges and limitations.

Don't be afraid to say no and move on and look for another place. If it doesn't feel right, move on. Your focus is on your group and if they feel comfortable and safe, they will return.

TYPES OF VENUES

With one of the previous businesses I owned, I did events, and trying to find a venue was one of the most difficult things to do. There is a lot involved, especially finding one that matches your needs. Since the venues I was looking at were of all sorts and sizes, they had to accompany a group of a dozen people to over a couple hundred.

So where do you begin this mission of finding a place for your practice group? Go back to your checklist (mentioned in the beginning of the topic of Venue), and list the top things that are important to you and your group.

Then make a separate list of places to have your practice group, and try to think in your mind if anything you listed of importance matches or stands out in your venue checklist. Maybe there is a place that does have free parking, and is easily accessible on your list of venues?

Here is a list of venues for you to look at to help you define some places near you that can be utilized for a Qigong practice group.

- **Place of Worship** - These establishments may not allow a group, unless you belong to their church. It doesn't hurt to ask. Find out if there are any restrictions. If you are not a member, you may be charged.
- **Hospitals** - See if there is some sort of health and wellness program for those who work at the hospital, or for their patients.
- **Retirement Communities** - These places will have some sort of committee that organizes events for their retirees. Start a dialog with them about what you do and how those who participate in the group can benefit from Qigong. Provide documentation if necessary.
- **Recreational Places** - A park might be a good idea, but think about the weather in this case. See if the park has an indoor place

to practice on those not so nice days of cold weather, rain, snow, etc.

- **Schools** - As an alumni, sometimes you can get good deals on room rental. Maybe offer the students attending school a free or reduced rate to join practice in exchange for the room at no charge.
- **Hospices** - Again, there may be a committee that you would have to talk to, or someone who is in charge. You will want to find the person in charge and talk with them. Bring a printout of your presentation and walk them through on what Qigong is all about. Leave handouts/brochures for them to review, so they can pass them on to others who make the final decision. They may also request for these to be in digital format to be emailed and shared with others.
- **Libraries** - Some libraries offer conference rooms for free, but I have found that they usually get booked out 6 months ahead of time by others who need a free room. Call your local library for more information.
- **At Your Place of Work** - They may have some sort of health & wellness program. Look at the bulletin boards to see if someone else is already doing some sort of wellness program and have a conversation with them to see how to get your program approved and advertised to the employees.
- **Hotel** - You can try and work out a deal to use one of their conference rooms, and maybe offer the hotel guests free access to practice in the morning or evening. In exchange, you can have a weekly practice group with your regular attendees and have new people (hotel guests) who wouldn't mind learning something new, or those who already do Qigong. Offer it to their customers for free and ask to get the conference room at no charge.
- **A Friends Place of Work** - Maybe your workplace is too small or they may not have an interest in someone teaching Qigong, but maybe there is a company where one of your friends work that already promotes a health and wellness program. They may be open-minded and willing to have someone come in and run a practice group.

Some companies would be happy to have someone facilitate

and teach Qigong for free. But if you are going to charge, they will ask for your instructor certification and past history of training certificates. Keep the originals of your certificates since they want to see these and make copies of them. When you continue to take additional classes on Qigong, keep your file updated so that it can be shared later when requested.

Expect a criminal background check before you start. This may take several weeks. A list of character references may be requested also. I have gone through this process before multiple times. Have at least 3 people listed with their contact information and present it right away when requested. Be prepared so things are not delayed. Also have a copy of any of your paperwork in digital format.

- **Home** - You can start a group out of your own home or at a friend's house. Keep in mind that your neighbors may have parking spots that they use frequently, and having a group of attendees absorbing these spaces may not be too favorable with them. If this could be a potential problem, ask your group to park at another location, or have them park in your driveway.

This is a good list to start with, build upon this and keep it just in case you have to find another location.

HOW TO BUILD YOUR PRACTICE GROUP

Here are some methods I would like to share that I have tried in the past and have been successful for me.

Look around you when you visit an establishment, and see if they have a bulletin board? Is there a place to put up announcements? Many of the coffee shops have an area to post something on their board. How about some of the colleges? Are there areas where students can post information about upcoming events? Maybe your local religious gatherings have a place to tack up an announcement. Many establishments have a central location where others can find out what is going on in their community. See if you can post your information there. Make sure you are not violating any rules or regulations. Always ask permission first.

While you are out and about visiting these places, you may notice an area where business cards are tacked to a cork board for visitors to take. Collect these. Just take one of each. This is a great start for building your email marketing campaign. You can make your announcements to these people about your Qigong practice group. Just remember to give people a choice to opt out from your emails. We'll talk a little more about this later.

Remember, many have not heard of Qigong, or know how to pronounce it when they read it. Keep in mind how you will deliver your message to your email list. Be careful not to lose them in Qigong terminology that they do not understand. Keep it simple for the layperson so they can get excited about what you have to offer. Other great locations to find business cards are health food stores; book stores, coffee shops, some bakeries, etc. Usually a place where people gather is a great place to let people know what you have to offer. At some of these places, you can even leave your business cards and fliers.

I have included some sample fliers on our website that compliments this book, and they are editable to help you start posting about your Qigong group.

Follow these bullet points below before you make your announcement. This will help you to effectively communicate your information before you print it out on paper, send in an email, or post on a website for others to see.

- What are you announcing? Create a big title/heading (here are some examples) - "NEED MORE ENERGY IN YOUR DAY TO DAY ACTIVITIES?" "DO YOU NEED A CHANGE IN YOUR LIFE?" "REMOVE ENERGY BLOCKAGES IN YOUR BODY" "WHAT IS QIGONG?"
- Where is the location of the class and what time does it start and end?
- How often is your group meeting?
- Who should they be looking for when they arrive?
- How do they contact you if they have an interest (phone and or email address)?
- What is Qigong and how would they benefit from it?

- If there is a cost associated with participating (example: first three sessions are free - inquire about pricing).
- Add at least one picture that is related to what you will be teaching. Having something visual and not having everything in all text will quickly draw someone in to read your announcement. Something that will pop out and grab someone's attention right away.
- Is there a prerequisite before attending your group?
- Is it for all ages? For teenagers and above? Age 50 and above? For a particular age group? Focused on a particular gender? Who are you targeting?

Try offering an overview class before starting your first group session. This would be a great way to spark interest and have people learn about Qigong before their first day. You can do an overview presentation on what Qigong is all about to help answer a lot of their questions and remove some of the mystery. You can present it in hospitals, retirement communities, recreational places, schools, hospices, churches, libraries, synagogues, or just about anywhere. Then direct them after your presentation to when and where you will be teaching Qigong. Have a flier to hand out in your overview class with information on your next practice group session and how often they meet.

The Qigong overview that I present is two hours long. I will go through the slides, answer questions, and then do the practice exercises along with a meditation. I get good feedback on the information presented, and some people notice some sort of sensation right away. Some have told me that they had noticed a change the very next day. But remember, results will vary. Others are intrigued about transforming energy to heal themselves, learning how to remove blockages, and how easy the exercises can be. Having group participation is also very helpful since people get a chance to be part of it and connect with others with similar interests.

Note: The PowerPoint presentation (on our website) that I use to teach an overview of Qigong gives people a taste of it before they join my weekly sessions. Feel free to tweak it for your own presentation style. I have also included handouts for your students, which will reflect much of the information within the presentation. Having handouts will save paper instead of printing out the entire presentation (which is about 2 hours long). These are the bullet points so that they can go back and reference them.

Qigong ebbs and flows my friend, it is something dynamic like the world we live in, so also reflect this in your presentation. You will discover new things on your path and may want to add your experiences to your teachings. If you do not wish to distribute the presentation (since you may frequently tweak it or want to avoid printing up reams of paper), and are asked by your students for copies, you can kindly tell them the handouts have the juicy stuff and will reflect much of what you will have talked about. Having too much information can overwhelm and they may lose interest.

Word of mouth is one of the best ways to help build your group. Once you have established a location, with a few people attending, they will soon be telling others about the class. Don't be afraid to tell people what you do, talk a little about Qigong, and give them your contact information.

TO DO AN OVERVIEW OR NOT

So should you do an overview before teaching a regular practice group? Should it be required for students to take a class before setting foot in your regular practice sessions? What should you do? For the most part, this is up to you. This all depends on the type of group you have. For myself, I require this for my regular practice groups. The reason? I think it's very important to prepare your students and empower them when they start something new. I have
noticed that this produces less confusion about Qigong.

I taught a practice group without doing a pre-session and people had a lot of questions during the practice. There are a lot of pieces to the puzzle that they are trying to put together. I find myself covering the basics almost every class. For example the stance, it could have been covered in the overview and additional time could have been devoted to other areas of Qigong. When you get new students, you may have to explain things over again while the other students have already heard it all before.

Offering frequent overviews (like once a month or more) will give people a chance to learn the basics, get many of their questions answered, and if they need a refresher, they can return to fill in some of those gaps. I have one group where the people are transitional. Meaning, they have been hospitalized or part of a program that runs for a limited time, they visit to learn and practice Qigong and then are discharged.

I sometimes end up giving them more information (handouts) at the end of class since they want to learn more and their visit to the hospital is brief. They are always welcomed to come back at any time. Since I run a practice group for a hospital that attracts people from multiple states, our time together can be short. But some end up getting a DVD to learn Qigong since it sparked an interest with them to help them continue to practice what they've learned. There are others who also frequently join since they may be there for a while due to their situation, or they have scheduled checkups on the day that practice is offered.

Explaining things over and over again eats away time from your class, and from your students while they are trying to get the full benefit of practicing. Telling people to pull energy to their lower dantian produces blank stares in the audience. What is a dantian and what does it do? Also never talk over your audience, meaning, use a lingo that they cannot understand. You may think you are nervous about teaching, but think about those who are learning. They too are nervous since they are starting something new. It can feel intimidating if you are using words that they don't understand. They will think people around them know more about what you are talking about than they do.

So my recommendation is to do your one-time overview of what the students will learn. They can get their questions answered on the spot and not have it come up over and over again in your session when new people arrive. I am not saying not to answer people's questions, they are encouraged. You want to help with the very basic and redundant questions to help further people.

If you do have someone who has not taken the overview and shows up for the class, you can explain to them that there is a required class before they can join your regularly scheduled practice. They are invited to stay, but they would most benefit from knowing the basics and being more knowledgeable about Qigong before getting more involved with it. Tell them when the next overview will be so they are aware of the next session.

If your audience is not attuned to what Qigong is in the beginning, you could spend more energy in areas that could take away class time and could have been done in an overview. Having many of the same questions answered in a single sitting, the Qigong overview could resolve this. You also may have things that you want to teach during your practice group time, but are unable to get to. There may be some confusion and questions or limited time during your regular sessions.

Don't get me wrong, you will get questions during practice, but having taken care of the basics will ensure you more quality time with your students. Over a period of time, without an overview - the dynamics of your group could change. If you come into a situation where you have to teach a practice group first, instead of the overview, teach the practice group session, but offer the overview for people at a later time. Let others know that the overview can expand their knowledge of Qigong and enhance their exercises. They will thank you in the long run and they will have more confidence in practicing and growing with Qigong.

I have done this before where the establishment wanted me to teach right away, then offer the overview classes later. Since the establishment wanted their participants to start benefiting right away, the overview would be scheduled for a future time.

With one of my groups that have transitional people, I do 5 minutes of the basics since about 90% of people are not regulars. If I notice that all the people are my regulars, I skip the 5 minutes of my presentation and dive right into Qigong, otherwise they will see the short presentation on the basics (the stance, what a dantian is, calling upon energy, etc.). I have pulled the basics from my slideshow and use this for the new people to quickly get them up to speed. I have reduced it to about 3-5 minutes long. I also use a smartphone, and connect my presentation to their big screen digital TV, which has been very helpful.

Each practice group is different and may have unique situations due to the environment you must work in. So doing an overview is up to you.

CHAPTER THREE
Marketing 101

"Know the Rules Well, so You can Break Them Later"
- Dalai Lama XIV

MARKETING 101: GETTING THE WORD OUT

When it comes to marketing, anyone can do it, and you don't need the big bucks to launch a marketing campaign. Keep it simple for you and your target market. I have learned much over the years as a business owner and entrepreneur, that this is one of the greatest and simplest secrets that was been given to me... **"Repetition Builds Retention"**. What I mean by this is that when you deliver the message to your audience, keep delivering the same message over and over again. I have seen some multi–billion dollar companies make such simple mistakes in this area that in the end it really costs them more money and the worst of it, they paid the highest price of all, losing customers.

For example, imagine a product you have been buying off the shelf for years. Maybe it's something from your childhood and you really love that brand name. Your mouth just waters for it, you have some set expectations, it's going to make your world complete for that one tiny moment in time (that slice of heaven), and you are going to invest your money and purchase it. Then you can't find it. You search and search and have no idea where it went.

You begin to panic because having that item brings back some pretty good childhood memories of you sitting in front of the television watching cartoons with your neighborhood friends (hang with me on this one), or having that feeling of a loved one that you miss taking care of you when you were sick. Then your brain goes into overload and finally after a long period of time of scanning up and down the aisles on the verge of walking away, the name brand pops out at you.

That bright yellow and red can that you have tattooed into your brain for all those years... After running up and down the aisle looking for it, your brain finally detects something different, the colors have now changed to black and brown. What the <bleep> happened? That repetition of that label over a period of time built retention in your mind and when it changed, your brain couldn't function.

You were programmed to look for that specific label and

during that entire time, your slice of heaven was right in front of your face. How frustrating. That product's image you had built up in your mind for all that time has gone away, and that one memory that was so important to you, just for that brief moment has just been crushed by that one changed item. Now you will have to reprogram yourself for the next encounter with this changed product, or find something better to build another memory you can hold on to. Breaking a habit takes a very long time before the code in your brain is written over.

This seems to be the new type of marketing these days; they decided to change something that has been marketed for many years, and now confuse their audience by changing one simple detail. Since your brain is branded, and blind to the change, you as the shopper decide to find another brand name (a competitor) because your brain was wired to find that first image burned in your mind. My advice to you, when you find something that attracts people, don't change it. Keep delivering that same message over and over again. That's called branding. Don't make this simple mistake that many companies are these days. They need to go back to the basics if they want to be successful again. Know thy audience. Repetition builds retention.

Once you get something going that is familiar to people, don't pull the rug out from underneath them by changing it and confusing them, keep the branding the same. This can be in a brochure, a business card, change in language (not using the same terminology passed onto you in your Qigong training), mixing other styles of Qigong into your teachings while you advertised a specific type you practice, etc.

So how do you help people find you? There are a few simple things that you can do. One of them is to get out there. Meet your audience. Once you find one person, they can lead you to another. Two people can lead you to many more. In just going out and meeting people, you can expand your market. I approached a university one day while living in Wisconsin, talked to them about Qigong, and they were very interested in having this taught in their health and wellness class. What was great about this, I offered it for free, and explained to them that I was giving back by doing community service before I become instructor certified. It was a Win-Win for the both of us.

Another way to tell people about your practice group is to go online and start posting on websites. There are many social websites that offer you the option of setting up your own group on just about any topic. Find one that enables you to receive an RSVP from your followers, the ability to post where your group will meet, has reminders that can be sent out to the group, and can be viewed by anyone in the general public. Of course, you want to make sure that people in your neighborhood are also utilizing that same website.

You might try finding some community websites you can post on, maybe a college website, a local message board, or maybe a group focused on health and wellness in your area. I have also included an area on our website for our readers to post their practice groups. Visit www.QigongWithJim.com, create an account, and tell us about your group and how others can contact you.

Word of mouth has been the best way for me to start any type of special interest group. Sit down, make a list of all the people you know (you may be surprised that you may hit a hundred). Go through that list and think of those who may have an interest and tell them what you're doing. Then talk to them. Maybe you're looking for a place to teach, you mention this in your conversation, and the other person on the end of the phone may know of an available place and join your class.

They may also know of someone who may be looking. Later on down the road, they will remember the conversation and refer them to you. Once you have a few people joining, don't be afraid to ask them to spread the word. Most people like to take a class and have someone they know attending it. Tell them that you are doing a free Qigong overview and they can invite someone to it. Once you get a few people who are enjoying the practice group, they will also be telling others.

Every time I have an overview coming up, I tell my students in the practice group about it, and they usually know of someone and invite them to it. Feel free to add some beverages and snacks after your overview (have people mingle afterwards) so they can meet others in the group. They will feel comfortable attending a practice group if they have met others with similar interests. They will already have a connection with someone on their first day of practice. Beverages, crackers, cheese and fruit have been successful for me.

Another direction might be to visit some of the health food stores and coffee shops, collect some of the business cards on the bulletin board, and start your own email campaign list. You can enter the names on your computer's email program (create a group) or use a third party that specializes in email lists. Make sure you don't share everyone's email address with each other when you send information out.

If you do, you just handed your own mailing list out to everyone and someone may use it for other purposes. Some people may not want their email address revealed. To find a service for email distribution, just use your favorite search engine and search for "Email Marketing Campaign", and you can pick through that list. Be sure you allow the option for people to opt out and the service has a way to track those who have read you emails, deleted them, forwarded them, etc.

I have used this technique of collecting business cards from all sorts of places in the past, sent out a broadcast message of an upcoming event, and people have shown up.

Another method to build your list is to go to some events, collect business cards, and add them to your mailing list. What type of event? There are a lot of free social networking events that you can visit, so find something that you have an interest in, but make sure you have your own business cards to hand out. Collect as many as you can. It's a little secret I learned some time ago in building my own mailing campaign to educate people on upcoming events, classes, and workshops while at social events. I have collected over 3,000 business cards; it helped grow my database for one of my businesses, and my monthly event attendance changed from 12 people to over 200. It took years of hard work, but well worth it.

You can also post your fliers at grocery stores, cafes, and just about anywhere that is accepting fliers. Make sure that yours stands out. Use very little wording, incorporate large letters, and always have the place, date, time, how people can contact you with questions, and if there is a charge. Having it too wordy will lose people. Give them the information quickly, up front, and easy to understand. You have about 5 seconds or less to make an impression in your advertisement, so make it count. There are also fliers included on my website for you to use and edit.

If you like working with the elderly, there are centers you can contact and share with them what you do. They will be happy to help market you to their senior citizens. Finding establishments that have an interest in having you teach their people (clients/customers); they will do most of the marketing for you, but also get involved with this so the right information is being communicated.

MARKETING AT YOUR OWN PLACE OF BUSINESS

Marketing at your place of business can be tough. Companies these days are big on health and wellness, but they may be too nebulous and you can't get support or have difficulty getting the word out to the employees. So my advice, seek out the person in charge of running the health and wellness program. Connect with them and tell them that you have been trained in Qigong, explain to them what it is, and that you would like to offer it free to the employees.

If you already have your instructor certification, some companies want to see this and sometimes ask if there will be a fee for your class. Some companies do have instructors that charge a fee to attend their classes. If you plan on doing this, have your fee structure in place. Be prepared before you have a conversation with the person in charge. Having everything all ready to go illustrates that you are well organized and prepared, and you're serious in what you do.

Before leaving, just give them one of your brochures or fliers so they can have something tangible to asses plus they can surf the Internet to find more information on Qigong. Feel free to add some of your favorite web-links to help get their questions quickly answered on Qigong. This will enable them to research without getting lost or finding incorrect information on the Internet. You can find some sample fliers also on my website for this book.

Before your first practice group starts at work, you may also be asked to hand out a waiver so the organization is not legally liable if someone gets hurt. Some companies already have one in place for you to use. If you don't have one, there is also one on my website. Make sure people sign these waivers and keep a folder of them for yourself. Be very organized in this area or you could end up being liable. I store mine at my desk under lock and key. You never know, there may be some sort of audit by the company, or they may just request a copy of the waivers. Always keep a copy or the originals for yourself.

Each place of business is going to be different in how they communicate their information to their employees. They may have a health and wellness section on their website, so try and get your group listed. They may also make frequent announcements or a newsletter. Get involved with this. I have been told that I cannot send out a mass email at work, but can put fliers in the break room, and other bulletin boards where I am allowed to hang up my literature. Some places may even have a bulletin board above the time clock so that when people punch in for work, they can see it.

Posting a flier in the break room does not give the best results and has rarely worked for me since people are too busy taking a break or eating, and in some cases, watching television - yes some companies have televisions in their break rooms. Advertising this way will produce low results, but it won't hurt to try it since you may get 1 or 2 people. Plus it is a quick reference on upcoming classes for current or new attendees.

Once your group starts growing, those in the group may point out your flier to others who may have an interest. I post the location and time on my fliers so folks know when classes are. At work, I have even created an email group for those who are attending, so I can send out announcements if I have an emergency, need to cancel, or if the room changes. Or ask people if they will be attending, especially near a holiday when people go on vacation and you may get no one showing up. Ask your Qigongers to reply to your email if they plan on attending the class.

One method I have tried is to form relationships with other managers to get the word out. I also have invited them to my overview. Some enjoyed Qigong and participated in the weekly practice group. You may always approach them and tell them that Qigong is part of the company's health and wellness program. Ask them if they can make an announcement at one of their general meetings? Managers are always having meetings. It doesn't hurt to ask and let them know that it has been approved by the business. It will no doubt be helpful in reducing workplace stress and getting people interested in participating in a group session.

You may also consider doing workshops on related Qigong topics several times a year to also spark interest. Once you get people participating, they can invite their friends, to learn more about Qigong.

MAKING MONEY

With any training, it may cost you hundreds of dollars (US dollars), but well worth it when you are first starting out. You may have to meet some minimum requirements before going out to teach your own Qigong group. But if you are looking at the instructor level, to get your certification, it may cost you around $10,000 or more. Think about the classes you spent money on, plane tickets to the retreats, the hotel stays, and the car rentals. This all adds up over time.

Since you may be new to Qigong, this is a great opportunity to learn it, study it, and view it as community service for others; to help spread the word. And in the process, build your skills in learning Qigong. You may not be allowed to charge students at that time since you may have to meet certain requirements before becoming certified, like having a minimum number of students per month that should be attending, how many people you have provided healing to, detection of blockages in the body, etc. Whatever the requirements, you will have to take tests to become Instructor certified. Once you have been certified, you are able to charge a fee. If you are looking to get qualified in teaching Qigong, you may have to visit websites to find an instructor in your area.

So what happens if during the first year (without your instructor certificate), you cannot find a place for free to teach and you decide to rent a place for your practice group. How do you cover this? One idea is to request "love donations" to keep the doors open. In other words, a donation given out of love and ability rather than obligation. Just keep in mind that this could be difficult, and you may not raise enough. It could be a struggle and you may end up paying most of the portion of the rental space, plus you may be involved with signing a contract. If this is something you want to do, go for it. But I just want to give you some insight of what could happen.

I myself like to avoid this type of scenario when it comes to renting. If your group starts downsizing or becomes non-existent, or maybe you are trying to build your group; it could take several months, you may end up with a bill for services that you are not using. Be very careful in this area. I would highly recommend finding something for free or for an exchange of services. Say for example, you teach Qigong at a chiropractors place, you offer the service for free for current patients and for those you invite, and you get a weekly place to teach.

This is a 3-way win. A win for the customer and your invites, a win for the chiropractor since it is an added value service which really doesn't cost them anything, and a win for you in that you have a place to teach. Think somewhere around exchanging services or doing it at a location that will not charge. Avoid contracts if at all possible and if you must have one, get an attorney or a real estate agent/broker to take a look at it, especially when it comes down to the fine print.

What if you are making a profit? Since you are not a certified instructor, you cannot charge people (per some Qigong teaching requirements). Now what? That was a similar question I had before. What about a website that accepts payments to cover the costs of running the web services and also renting a room? What if I was starting to make a profit? A suggestion came about to donate the money to a worthy cause, but let people in your practice group know ahead of time where the donated money would go before they signed up. My suggestion would be to keep a spreadsheet so the group can see where the money is going in case they asked. I thought that was pretty fair for all.

The only drawback is that you have to maintain records and there is a chance that someone could dispute it and/or want the money to go to another charity. If you can avoid handling any money that is donated, I would recommend it. You may come up with a better idea/solution, so give it some thought and see where it can take you before you make this type of decision.

So you completed the minimum requirements to start a practice group, you have been running your group without charging, and it has been going for over a year..... So what happens when you get your instructor certificate? Do you start charging your current practice group right away? How are your students going to feel about this? One problem you may run into is that some people may not be willing to pay since it was free to begin with.

If this is the general perception, your audience may begin to downsize. So what can you do to prepare for this? There are a few options here. Before you build your first group, think about what your goal is. Is this group free of charge and always will be? Or do you plan on charging later on? And if so, when?

You may want to consider having one group that is free (giving back to the community), and maybe have it designated towards those who are in great need, like a hospital, hospice, crisis center, etc. I would keep it free, but start a new group somewhere else and market that one with a fee to attend.

If you only have one location, inform those who are joining that you are offering it for free to build the group, but at a later date that you will be charging. Inform them what rate it will be, even offer them a discount. Plan ahead. If you have a date in mind of when the instructor certificate program will begin, you can set a date of when you will start charging after you receive your certificate. Then people won't be shocked.

You may lose a few people since the expectation was set when it was offered for free and then it changed. Don't worry, you can always rebuild your group. As long as you have a good quality group, people will keep coming back and refer others. But those students who invest their money into something, want something out of their investment, so keep this in mind.

The option of charging or not is up to you and if you do take money, don't feel guilty about it. It took a lot of hard work to train yourself (classes, seminars, workshops, etc.), including driving time and filling your tank to attend classes, maybe you spent money on airline tickets and hotel expenses. You have invested your time and hard earned money into getting certified, so it's okay to have a supplemental income and recoup what you invested in.

BUSINESS CARDS

For someone who will be teaching Qigong, and for others who want to learn more about it from you, I would highly recommend getting business cards. They don't have to be fancy, but just having the basics such as your contact information would be most useful. When I teach classes, I have people who sometimes ask me where to find more information, so I give them my business card. It will direct them to my website which tells them about my class times, and links to the Qigong website (the style you learned) to help them learn more, or even purchase a DVD, music, and other merchandise. Some Qigong organizations have affiliate programs so you can earn a little extra money.

If you don't want to give out your phone number, I would recommend setting up a free account under Google Voice and get a phone number. With Google Voice, you can get a virtual number and have it forwarded to your home, work, or cell number. I use this for myself. You have control over where you can forward your calls, it will email you a transcript of any voice messages, plus you can still keep your cell and home phone private. If you don't like to give out your personal numbers, this method would be a way to go. With google voice, it also enables me to screen my calls and eliminate phone spammers.

The business card is one of the best methods of allowing someone to reach out to you and enables people to share your contact info with others. Plus you can post it on bulletin boards for others to grab, and quickly distribute to a crowd of people (like a social networking event). You may also leave your business card in fishbowls to win a free lunch at your favorite place to eat.

On my website there is a free program for the Avery business card stock which includes a sample business card template, so you can design your own cards and print them. This will help get you started right away and design it the way you want it.

Sample Business Card

You can also order business cards on the Internet, and some are free, but in some cases include a small advertisement on the back. As long as you have something that can be portable, has your contact information, and can quickly be passed around, it is well worth it, plus it's really inexpensive.

When you design a business card, make sure you leave some room for people to take notes. If something is of importance, people will find something to write on, like a business card. Leave plenty of space to help accomplish this. You never know when someone wants to leave you with some information, like a contact name and number.

Just have the basics on your card, like your name, number, email address, and website if you have one. Make it easy for people to contact you, plus easy to read. Good luck.

TIP: How to get a dedicated phone number for your own practice group for free? I use a service by Google, so people with questions can call me or leave a voice message (like questions on practice group meeting times or if they are unable to attend). It's great if you don't want to give out your home or work phone number. To do this, visit www.Google.com/voice and create an account. If you have an existing Google/Gmail account you can use that profile to set up a new phone number anywhere in the USA and have that new phone number transfer calls to any other number, like your cell or home phone.

It says after you sign up:

"Google Voice gives you a single phone number that rings all of your phones, saves your voicemail online, and transcribes your voicemail to text. Other cool features include the ability to listen in on messages while they're being left, block unwanted callers, and make cheap international calls. We hope you enjoy using Google Voice"

CONFERENCE CALLS

When you have a lot of experience under your belt and if you are looking at expanding in teaching others about Qigong, start a monthly conference call. It doesn't have to be big, but something local with a handful of people joining in. Over time it could grow. This is a great way to reach out to others that are not in your group and a great opportunity for those who join to meet others and learn more about Qigong.

There are some free conference call phone numbers on the Internet, but long distance charges may apply to those who would be calling. These will not be 1-800/866/888 numbers, but regular phone numbers with area codes. You may find one available in your area. Just do a search on "Free Conference Calls" in your favorite search engine.

You can also get others to participate and help you on the call. Reach out to others who are experienced in Qigong and interview them on the conference call, then open it up to questions. After the Q&A, do a meditation for everyone. If you have ever listened to other conference calls on Qigong, try a similar format or create your own. Listen to a few of these calls to get a better understanding on how you would like to structure yours.

Doing conference calls is another way to reach out to others who have an interest in Qigong. You may even get some local people who are interested in joining your group or they may find out about other groups in their area.

A great way to create a following is to announce that you have a monthly conference call where your students and others can join in to listen to a session that will help improve their Qigong. An example would be to just talk about a single exercise. Say for example that you decide to do a conference call in June and the topic would be about the exercise – Balancing Yin and Yang.

Go through the steps on how you do it, but also tell them the benefit of the exercise. Even have your audience join in the exercise while they are listening. What does this exercise do? What is the meaning of the column of light that you are supposed to imagine? What does the moving of your left and right hands do? What parts of the body are Yin and Yang? Slowly explain and have each one follow on the call. This may take about 5 -10 minutes. Then go into a meditation and have others join you. Do this for each exercise in explaining the benefits of what each one does, or have one of your guests go into great detail about it for you.

If you like, you can incorporate some background music (make sure it is low enough so others can hear you) during your meditation, or when teaching something that has long pauses. I was on a meditation conference call one day, the meditation was longer than expected and it felt like we went over our time. When I looked, my call was disconnected. I did not know the call was dropped, since there was a lot of dead air spots during the conference call and meditation.

To avoid losing your audience, and to give them a chance to dial back in so they don't miss anything, use low background music. This will be a great way to signal people so they will know that they got disconnected, and an excellent way to fill the dead air if there will be long pauses, or no talking during the meditation.

TIP: Pre-record your calls. If you are a perfectionist, feel free to record your talking track, edit it, and put some background music into it. Then play it for your audience. You can complete 12 sessions, and then play one of them each month. This can give you that advantage of not scrambling trying to figure out what you are going to do for that particular month.

Having it already planned ahead of time will make things easier for you and your audience. You can play it over the conference call and when done, do some live Q&A. Knocking out a whole bunch of these on the same day can save you a lot of time. Plus you can have them as an MP3 for others to download and listen to them.

*   **TIP:** On the technical side, make sure you test everything before you introduce it to your audience. Be prepared. Don't have the embarrassment of doing your call and no one can hear you or your recording. Maybe you decide to stream it over the Internet so others can listen to it live. Make sure you test this on several computers and let people know what the minimum requirements on their computer should be to listen to you. Over time you'll become an expert. You may even incorporate online presentations for people to view while you or your guest talks about a particular topic and take questions.*

30 SECOND COMMERCIALS

You're at a table with a group of people, they want to get to know who you are. They ask what your hobbies are and you reply that you teach Qigong. They all glance at each other with confusion since they have not heard of this term before and wonder what it is. They ask.... Is it a martial art? Chinese pottery? A new type of diet? Is it some kind of health food?

When you are asked the question "What is Qigong?" How will you answer?

Trying to answer this question can make you nervous in how you describe it to them. What do you tell them? Where do you begin? What information could you communicate that would not lose the person who asked the question? Would they understand? So many thoughts can funnel through your mind and picking out the right words so these people will understand your answer could be difficult. So what do you do?

In the business world, the way we quickly tell someone about who we are and what we do is called the 30 second commercial, or the elevator speech. This an effective way to get your message across within 30 seconds. Why 30 seconds? The reason is that most people have a small attention span. Do you ever wonder why most of your commercials are 30 seconds? They are trying to get your attention in a short period of time to deliver an important message. Why do they call it an elevator speech?

Just imagine that you are the owner of your own company.

You have a product or service that you are trying to sell to another company. One day, you decided to visit the 'ABC Company' that you know will benefit from you service. You have attempted many times to get an audience with them, but every time you go there, they tell you that the president of the company is unavailable. It has been the same routine for several months, unable to tell anyone in that company about your service.

Usually, you get on the elevator after you've been refused a meeting, you're on the top floor and you want to get to your destination - the parking garage. You step in, push the ground level button, the doors closes. As the elevator is moving, it stops at a floor, and a very professional looking person gets on. You recognize them as the President of the company. They are in the elevator next to you, so now is your chance. You now have about 30 seconds to deliver your message to the President of this company before they reach their next floor.

So what do you say to win this person over so they know exactly what you do and spark an interest so they will use your services? Now it's time to use your elevator speech.

I have prepared a few responses below that will help get you started so you can build confidence in explaining to people, in a very short period of time, what Qigong is, and possibly start opening up a dialog. Pick one below and practice your 30 second commercial until you feel comfortable with it. Here are some examples that you can use:

"Qigong is Traditional Chinese Medicine passed down through the generations which dates back thousands of years. Qi (chee) in Chinese means energy, and Gong (gung) means work. So I teach people how to work with and remove energy blockages in their body using low-impact exercises."

"Qigong is energy work that removes blockages which helps balance and heal the body. Qi means "energy", and Gong means "work" in Chinese. It basically means working with energy. I teach people several techniques using low-impact exercises to help reduce stress and tension. I also incorporate meditation in my classes to help build focus and increase awareness."

"I teach Qigong to people to help balance their energy, reduce stress and tension, and increase their awareness. Qigong in Chinese means "working with energy" and the techniques I show have been passed down from ancient Qigong masters from thousands of years ago. It will change your life forever. "

"Qigong is an integrated Chinese medicine that helps people remove energy blockages in their body. It consists of low impact exercises, meditation, visualization, breathing and sound, to balance and increase the flow of energy in the body."

"Qigong is an ancient Chinese method of doing simple body movements, visualization, breathing, and sound, to balance the energy in your body and also help remove blockages. It is a complimentary medicine that can be done by anyone in group or in the privacy of their own home."

"I work with people to help reduce stress and tension in their lives, giving them simple tools to help balance their energy, increase focus and awareness. I teach a class using ancient Chinese body movements and exercises to help my students increase their energy flow. It's called Qigong. To break it down, Qi means energy, and Gong means to cultivate. So in other words, practicing Qigong will cultivate and increase a person's vitality and energy to help improve the overall balance and enjoyment of life."

Feel free to use any of these, or grab some key words that stand out for you and create your own mini-commercial to help people get a better understanding of Qigong. It will help you build more confidence in what to say as more people ask you about Qigong. These key words would also be great in a social networking environment when people ask you, especially when you are in an elevator, in a small group, or at an event.

Have something prepared and practiced ahead of time so you can effectively communicate what you do and to open the door for people who would have an interest in learning Qigong. On my website, there are additional 30 second commercials. Since it's in electronic format, you can load them up and play around with the words that sound best to you.

CHAPTER FOUR
Fine Tuning (The Details)

"Sayings Remain Meaningless Until
They are Embodied in Habits"
- Kahil Gibran

BEING SMART ABOUT YOUR GOALS

Goals are very important, especially when you are going to start a Qigong practice group. What is your vision of the group? Where will it take you and your students? How long are you going to run the group? What do you want to accomplish? Is it catered to a particular group of people, like pregnant mothers, the disabled, people over a certain age, just for anyone, etc.?

If you don't have a goal in mind, you don't have a focus. If you're not focused on an end result, you will keep spinning your wheels, and end up putting more energy into something then you really should. It can become frustrating and you may never reach your goal. This could result in a failed Qigong practice group.

In the project management world, there is an acronym used - S.M.A.R.T., which stands for **S**pecific, **M**easurable, **A**ttainable, **R**ealistic, and **T**imely. This helps you identify specific goals, and using the acronym helps create steps in getting you towards your goal and accomplishing it. This method was created by George Doran, Arthur Miller, and James Cunningham. Try using this method for your goals before you start your practice group, it will produce far greater results. Since your group will be dynamic, you should always check your goals.

Don't just have one set of goals when you start, and then stop there. Continue redefining your goals. For example, after a year, take a look at what you've done. What has been successful or not? What can you do to improve your group? Look at it as a business. See your attendees as customers. What are their needs? What are their goals with Qigong? What are the things that they want to accomplish and can you help them get there? What services can you provide and keep your customer base thriving?

There is always change in the air and you have to re-examine your group frequently to adapt to those changes. Also, try using SMART goals to look towards the future. How do you see your group in one year, three years, in five to ten years? When you have a very successful group, and you want to start another, use your SMART goals to start a new group.

It may not be the same as your first, or it may be exactly the same, but you want to duplicate it in another location. SMART goals can be short-term or long. It can be done in a few days, months, a year or more. It's kind of like laying out your business plan.

Let's get down to SMART goals and what you need to define them.

Specific: Your specifics have to be clear and concise. It is focused on an outcome and not the process of getting there.

Ask yourself.....

- What do you want to accomplish?
- Who will be responsible for this task?
- What's going to be required to get you there?
- What are the constraints?
- What are the final objectives and benefits?
- Where will it take place?

Example: *I want to start a successful Qigong practice group for those with physical challenges, at a location that is near my work, and is convenient in time and distance.*

Measurable: A measurable goal uses steps that can be personally managed or delegated. When using steps, these can be monitored to see your progress. This also helps you to keep on track to meet your deadlines, and reach your target dates.

Ask yourself.....

- How are you going to measure this to determine your success?

- How will you know when it is accomplished?

Example: *I want to build my group to around 20 people within the first 9 months.*

Attainable: Basically, is your goal realistic? Is it out of your reach? Is it pointless? Will it stretch past your capabilities? Try to identify what goals that are going to be the most important to you and determine if what you're asking for is truly attainable.

Ask yourself....

- How can this goal be accomplished?
- Do I need additional resources to help get me there?
- What skills or training is needed?

Example: *I will find a location that will accommodate between 20-25 people, which is within a reasonable distance between my work and home.*

<u>R</u>elevant: Your goal must be based upon the current conditions and realities of the environment. Choose your goal that matters. It aligns your values and determines if this is worthwhile. When relevant goals are met, it will move your forward.

Ask yourself.....

- Is this relevant?
- Does this align with other efforts or needs that you have in place?
- Is the timing right?

Example: *By achieving this goal, it will give me the ability to teach others with physical challenges, enable them to learn Qigong to help heal themselves, and have the ability to meet others who are in similar situations like myself since I was recently disabled.*

<u>T</u>ime-bound: Having a specific date/time is important. Many people do not make it this far due to the day-to-day chaos that arises. Give yourself a committed time on when your goal will be accomplished. Set yourself a target date. This will help you focus more on when your goal will be completed.

Ask yourself....

- When will this goal be completed?
- For each step, what is the scheduled date of completion for these?
- How often will these time targets be monitored?
- What can I do today to make it happen tomorrow?

Example: ***This goal will be completed on Saturday, July 11th, 2020.***

Now with everything in place, you can put together a summary to help better define your statement of what your goal is and how you are going to accomplish it.

My SMART Goal:

To start a successful Qigong practice group that is focused on those with physical challenges in their lives. I will grow this group to around 20-25 people within the next nine months with a deadline of July 11th. This group will be within a 5 mile radius around my work or home, with convenient hours that will work with my job schedule. By accomplishing this goal, this will enable me to meet others with similar disabilities and allow me and my participants to grow in practicing Qigong together.

There is also a downloadable document on the website for this book that will help you with your S.M.A.R.T. goals in setting up and continuing your Qigong practice group(s).

SETTING UP

Do you have enough chairs? Are there things that need to be moved? Is the sound system working? Do you have a CD changer or a sound system that you need to get training on?

Arrive 15-20 minutes before your start time and prepare for your session. Remember, this time goes real fast when you are setting up. If you can get others to help while they are arriving, don't be afraid to ask. Maybe you have a session of 15-20 people and the chairs just arrived. Ask for some volunteers to help lend a hand in setting them up. The quicker you can get this completed, the less chance that doing this will eat into everyone's time.

When you get to your destination, you never know what the conditions of the room will be when you get there. I have been locked out of rooms and trying to get a hold of someone who has a key. There have been times when the room has been reserved by another group (especially in the corporate world) or you have some out-of-towners that have set up camp in the room and are on a very important conference call. You never know what to expect when you arrive.

If you arrive and there is another class ahead of you in the room and it is getting close to your time, just walk in the door and politely ask when they will be finished so you can setup for your class. If they go into overtime (hopefully not and they respect your time), you may have to find another room. Expect the unexpected. If you have to reserve a room, and your class starts at 5 pm for example, reserve it for 4:45 pm to give yourself time to set up. Look for areas around the building beforehand, or while you are visiting, and pick out a spot or two. Do this just in case you need a backup if your room is not available.

I have ended up going outside on a nice day since I did not have access to the room and practiced with the group while people walked by. If you love getting attention, this will definitely work.

You may have to do some set up of your music, or maybe doing a presentation and need to make sure the equipment is also working. If you are working with technical equipment that's not yours, I would arrive at least a minimum of 30 minutes to make sure everything is set up and ready to go. The earlier you can get there to set up, the less problems you will have when your session begins. You don't want to end up running into technical difficulties with a projector, the sound system or you need to have Internet access. It may become an issue when class starts and could delay you session.

If you will be doing healing on people in the room, make sure there is room for you to walk around them. When I get to my room, I have to move furniture out of the way, and space the chairs out so I can walk around people. I have bumped into walls, chairs, tables, and other objects. So get there early and be prepared.

MISTAKES

Are you worried that you'll make mistakes while teaching? Of course you will, and that's okay. Just remember to do the best you can do.

I find myself missing some things, like a talking point I wanted to bring up, or what the results of a particular exercise will perform. I still make mistakes, even when I have done over 500 days straight of practicing Qigong exercises. Just learn from your mistakes, and move on.

So what do you do when you miss something during the exercises? Simple....keep going! No need to stop the show. You can get it the next time. Your audience may not even notice. If they do, no big deal. If you feel guilty, just let it go or go back to it later. You're not doing any disservice to your group. I notice over time that, yes I make mistakes. We are all just human anyways.

At the beginning of an exercise, I think to myself "What is going to be the next exercise"? This will give you time while you're doing the current exercise to find the next one. Since you're doing it in the very beginning, there is less pressure on yourself in finding the next one. If you don't remember, what is the exercise after the one you forgot? Just go for that one. You'll do just fine.

If you notice mistakes performed by other group leaders/instructors, please don't point them out during the class. They may have already realized it. If it is something that you feel is incorrect and should be talked about, approach the leader after class without any students around. Respect them, don't embarrass them. We are here to help each other grow.

HAVING NO CLASS

It's finally happening and you are slowly getting people to come to your practice group. Week after week, there are people attending. You have struggled very hard at keeping your group alive and then one day, nobody shows up for your class. Is it a good time to panic? Did you do something wrong? Absolutely not. Please don't feel that people don't have an interest, they do.

There will be times when you will have one, a few, and many that will attend. Understand that everyone has their own lives and responsibilities that will not mirror your own. There are busy schedules, emergencies happen, there are immediate schedule changes, and other forms of chaos that happens in people's lives, or they just don't feel like doing Qigong that day. You worked so hard in getting people to attend and then, one day, no one shows. Don't take it personal.

For example, I was waiting for my students....... Waiting.......Waiting....... And nothing. I gave everyone an extra 10 minutes, but not a single body walked through the door. I was a bit disappointed, but realized that I could take the time to do something related to Qigong. Maybe practice since I have the room booked, or work on organizing my folder of handouts, or looking through a self-healing pressure point book and take some notes for my next class. It was nice to have some me time and to do a little catch up.

For myself, I have an uncanny sense of when people are going to show up or not (meetings, classes, appointments, etc.) or I am supposed to be some place for some reason. One day, I was getting this feeling that someone was supposed to be here (at class), but I had no shows. I waited, but nothing. Weird I thought, I still have this feeling. I decided to do a little practice and then leave. Before I leave, I usually talk to the security guard (this was at my work, so security is pretty tight) to see how things are going in general.

After teaching several classes, I started to get acquainted with our new security guard in the evening. When I was leaving, I asked them how things were going. They told me that they were admitted to the emergency room the day before, due to high blood pressure. They were having severe headaches and became blind in one eye. As I was hearing their story, I remembered the week before, during our Qigong practice group, I was showing the technique on how to lower/raise blood pressure.

This is a technique that's I learned in one of my Qigong classes. I showed them how it worked and said that if they had that same feeling again, try this technique, but also seek medical attention since they almost had a stroke the last time. So if you find yourself alone, there may be a reason behind it. You may not know what for, and it may not make sense, so I guess my intuition alerted me to someone who could benefit from Qigong, even though I had no shows for that evening.

People, who attend your class, are supposed to be there. That's how I look at it. Even if you have one person. Don't worry if people are not showing up. If it happens in succession for 4-5 times, consider looking at why people are not attending. Maybe the time class starts is not good for these people, or the length is too long, or could it be that something else is turning people away?

Around the holidays, I get a small group that shows up, even just one person, or sometimes there are none. It gets busy in people's lives during these times. I would not factor this in if you have low attendance or none. If you have built up relationships around some of these people, contact them. They will probably be honest with you and let you know what is happening.

Also take a look at how you are marketing your group to see if this needs some tweaking. Maybe the word isn't getting out yet.

PUNCTUALITY

Sometimes you'll have people that have questions before the practice begins, and some just enjoy chatting. That's okay, but you must start on time. Respect those around you since someone may be on a busy schedule. Start on time and end on time. I would also recommend the same for your students. You may have someone that is chronically late, and you can tell by the energy in the room that it's disturbing people. If they are showing up late while everyone is practicing, this throws everyone off, especially if the group is already doing their meditation.

As a group leader, I strongly suggest that you arrive much earlier than your students. Be the example. You may have a group that allows for stragglers (like at a crisis center, hospice, hospital, etc.), and this should be expected. Since I work with disabled military veterans, I get people that will show up 10 minutes late. Just keep the flow going, but if they become very disruptive in the class, you will have to have a conversation with them or ask them to leave.

I remember during a yoga class I was taking, the room was filled with people doing a meditation. A lady in her mid-50's arrived about 15 minutes late. She looked like she was in a panic and in a big rush. She brought in her duffle bag, and inside of it was her yoga mat, and some plastic bags.

While she was digging around for her stuff, you could hear these noisy bags, making a loud crinkling cellophane noise across the room. She was frantically pulling things out of her bag and oblivious to the fact that she was being very loud and it was very disruptive to the class. She laid things out, and during the class, she kept going through her bag, putting things back in because she kept forgetting something.

About 10 minutes before the end of class, she packed her things up, making the same disturbing noises, and rushed herself out. It was very rude, disruptive, and took away the enjoyment of the class. Just imagine this same person repeating this event every time you have a class. Do you think over a period of time there would be a decline in attendance? As a group leader, you should step in and politely have a conversation with them if this continues.

I wanted to share this story with you and to empower you so that you don't end up in situations like this that could take away the quality of your group. Just imagine your entire group meditation, you're completely relaxed and focused. You feel like you are part of the universe. Then someone starts packing their things up and leaves and generating loud sounds that could impact your meditation. Or someone arrives making noise while you are balancing yin and yang and you are at a higher point of meditation that you have never before achieved.

Be the leader of your group and try and work out problems as they arise. Don't wait until later. If there is something going on that your group is having trouble with, see if you can resolve it right away. You will earn your groups respect if you act upon whatever the trouble is in a very timely manner. This could be a lack of chairs for your group, the person who is responsible for opening up the door is hardly on time, the bathrooms are locked so you or your students are unable to use them, etc.

To help guide those who are having trouble being punctual, on our website, you will find a sign you can hang up outside your door to inform people that class is in session, and to please not disturb the session. Hopefully this should be helpful in reminding people that class is in session and they can attend the next available one.

TWEAKING YOUR PRESENTATION

If you use the presentation from our website, or use your own, feel free to adjust it over time. You may have different ones depending on the group you are doing your introductory overview with. You will be learning more about Qigong over time and you may want to share it with your audience, this is where the adjustments come in (adds, deletes, updates).

You may have learned that the medical industry published their results on Qigong and its effects. Hey, that's great news, incorporate it into your presentation, have it part of your handouts or a talking point. I have tweaked my presentation several times to match my audience or I may think of something important that they should be aware of.

I do an overview of Qigong just about twice a month. I am always trying to perfect it and I try to put myself in the shoes of my audience, plus use their feedback. It helps me make sure that I am not talking over their heads and not losing them in what I am showing them.

Or they may not understand something. Just remember the many questions you had when you first learned about this healing modality. They may have similar ones as you did. Since you're currently starting out new with learning Qigong, right now is the best opportunity to scan your presentation and say to yourself "If I am new to Qigong, would this make sense to me?"

Over time, your presentation is going to expand and condense. I teach a class where I have taken information from my two hour presentation on Qigong, and reduced it to about 5 slides, since the audience is constantly changing. Since one of my groups is at a hospital, my attendees change a bit since some are in for a short period of time due to their injuries. It takes 5 minutes of their time to quickly get them up to speed on the basics so they can dive in and participate.

SPEED-QIGONG

Sometimes while you're practicing, you'll have a few that speed things up during some of the exercises, especially if you have a small group and it's very noticeable. You may feel a little pressured, but hold your course. Just remember, you're the leader of the group. If people feel like rushing through the exercises, let them. Just maintain the speed you feel comfortable teaching. Soon the ones that are rushing through will adjust their pace and slow down.

You'll also notice others that are at a slower pace. The same thing with them, maintain your velocity. You can't adjust to everyone's speed. You are the centerpiece of attention and providing direction. You may notice at times where everyone is harmonized and in synch with each other. This won't happen overnight or all the time. It takes time for everyone who are starting out new to learn all the motions and feel comfortable doing it on their own.

ROLE MODELING

As a Qigong group leader, you should be a role model for others. This is very important for the longevity of your group. Students will look up to you, ask questions, and at times want to be like you. They are looking for the goodness in people, someone they can trust, and someone they can go to with questions. You will be a mentor for these people and help guide them. We have all had questions and looking for guidance when practicing Qigong.

How does that particular exercise go? Why do I have to have my back straight? Why should I keep a smile on my face?

Having someone to go to helps them with their own personal growth, and supports them on their journey. Being chronically late, telling people they are doing it wrong, raising your voice at them, showing up intoxicated, making sexual advances on your students, etc. This is not a good role model. People will gravitate to you, and it will grow along with the quality it deserves, if you respect others, Qigong, and yourself

Set the example by being there before your students arrive, be punctual and start on time and end on time, run a very organized and structured group. Setting the right tone, others will copy, and when they go off and start their own group someday, they will look back at the wonderful experience they had with yours and share the same leadership experience within their own group. They too will pass along the baton with same good qualities to their students as you did with yours.

The very best role models makes people see the possibilities within themselves. You can really influence those around you by the way you show your passion and vitality in what you do. As a group leader, you want to make the lives of others better, and this shows in how you interact with others within your practice group. Show love, kindness, compassion, respect, and forgiveness. These are very strong qualities that others can learn from you.

Just remember, as a role model, you will learn from others, but also learn a lot about yourself. My granddaughter told me one day while driving in the car, that I am a great mentor to her. She expressed that she has learned a lot from me, especially when it comes to business. She remarked that she will apply these skills when she becomes the owner of the Cardinals baseball team someday. This is great stuff coming from a seven year old. I have made a great impact in her life.

I taught her a very simple skill one day.... to say people's names when she first meets them. For one thing, people like to hear their name, they like to be recognized and appreciated. This is a great skill that she has learned. Every time we go out to a restaurant, she will read their name tags and call them by their names. "Cindy, thank you for the french-fries", "Dan, may I have another glass of water?", "Rita, may I have more ketchup?" I just look at their faces, their jaws just drop and these people are in shock, and then you see the gratitude on their faces of someone so small and innocent recognizes them for their hard efforts. It sure makes an impression.

Here is a seven year old kid using the simplest form of communication, by just saying their names, and it brings big smiles on their faces and brightens their days for that very one moment in time. She also feels so proud of herself and now it has become a game to see their reactions and getting nice compliments. It's now fun to her and I compliment her every time in doing it. She will do great in business someday. She has been doing this for a few years now and she will be great at remembering names when she gets older, and a role model to others. I am sure she just blows away the other adults when she does this when I am not around.

So be a role model to others. You will notice people in your group will be looking up to you.

CHAPTER FIVE
Defining Your Practice Sessions

*"Your Treasure House is in Yourself,
it Contains all You Need."*
- Hui Hai

TALKING POINTS DURING PRACTICE

While teaching Qigong, what do you say to your students while they are practicing? What do you point out during a particular exercise while you are all doing it at the same time? What are the tips that you pass along to them while performing Qigong?

This chapter will go through some sample bullet points for students while they are practicing, along with some tips to help you out.

So just imagine that you are doing one of the basic the exercises with your practice group. While you are all in the stance, what little reminders do you give your students?

Incorporating bullet points during the exercise is part of the repetition that helps build retention at every session. Repeating these bullet points during each session will help those practicing become familiar in how to perform each of the exercises. There is a lot to learn, and going over them frequently will help build confidence in your participants, and it will empower them in better understanding the inner workings of Qigong.

While going through each exercise, walk them through it, but give it a few seconds to sink in, and give them time to perform it before you move on to the next bullet point.

Let's start out with that basic exercise you have in your mind for example: "Bend at the knees", *then give yourself about 5 seconds (so people who forgot to bend at knees can do so), then...* "Now focus on your dantian", *allow 5 more seconds (this gives people time to check themselves),* "Keep your shoulders relaxed", *another 5 seconds passes,* "Put your tongue on the roof of your mouth", *another 5 seconds passes by,* "Put a smile in your heart", *etc.*

Don't worry if you miss a few. You can get them the next time. Look around your group as they are practicing. If you see a few people who are standing up straight - with their knees locked, you don't have to point these individuals out to the group, you can just say to the entire group in a soft voice "Remember to bend at the knees". If people look tense, say "Remember to drop and relax your shoulders, that's where people hold a lot of their tension and stress".

Help guide your students while you are teaching a practice group. You can modify it to however you want, but these are just guidelines to help those who are just starting out. Below is some of the key content that practice group leaders say to their audience. You don't have to say it all at once before you begin the exercise, but use the bullet points that you create throughout the exercise, with some pauses in between, and give it time to sink in. Feel free to visit other groups to see how they do it and if you like something you hear, duplicate it for yourself.

What's presented below is part of the repetition that helps build retention during your sessions.

Here is a sample bullet points with small snippets that are said during a session.

Basic Standard Qigong Stance

- "Empty your mind"
- "Put a smile on your face or in your heart"
- "Have your feet shoulder width apart"
- "Keep your spine straight"
- "Have a slight bend at your knees"
- "Keep your shoulders dropped"
- "Breathe through your nose"
- "Imagine that healing energy is coming from the universe when you breath in"
- "Pull this energy towards your dantian"
- "Just imagine that you are breathing through your skin and that the energy is healing every cell in your body as it's moving towards your lower dantian"
- "When you exhale, visualize that your blockages and pain are exiting every pore of your body, pushing it towards the ends of the universe, never to come back again"

Announcement for Those That are Pregnant

There are exercises that are not recommended for pregnant women. Just make the basic announcement before starting that particular exercise. For example:

- "For those whom are pregnant, you may skip this exercise. Otherwise, while performing it do the following……. (demonstrate if necessary)

So take the time to map out what little snippets you can announce to your group during each exercise you perform. This will help them with retention on how each exercise is performed. I have a list of bullet points that I use for each Qigong exercise so it keeps me in check and helps my students get familiar in what to do for each exercise. After a while, you may not have to do this unless you get a new student and have to talk about how to do each exercise again.

Below are some sample Qigong sessions that you can use as an outline for your own practice group.

SAMPLE ONE HOUR QIGONG PRACTICE SESSION

6:14 PM

Hang the "Please Do Not Disturb" sign(s) on the entrance(s) to the room

The sign states to come back the next time since the class is currently in session. The signage is used to respect your student's time and also not have your class interrupted while in session. If your students cannot show up on time, that's on them. Tell your students that you value their time, your classes will start at a particular time, and that your expectation of others is to be punctual. If they cannot be there on time, you will be happy to see them at the next practice day. A sample "Do Not Disturb" sign can be found on our website.

6:15 pm

Why start at 15 minutes past the hour? I do this to give people some extra time to prepare before class. You don't have to do this, but it is something I have experimented with and it works out well. Sometimes you will have people that show up 5-10, or even 15 minutes late. Starting 15 minutes past the hour has been successful for me. Some people finish at work on the hour and arrive at or before a quarter after the hour. Sometimes you'll have students arriving before you do. Remember, be on time for your class. Be there early before the class starts so this gives you time to prepare, set up any equipment (like music) and answer questions from your students.

At this time, start your Qigong session. I begin with some quick movement exercise for warming up. Some groups will spend about a minute or longer doing this. It all depends on how much time you have slotted for you session (one hour or two, or more).

For example, I would bounce up and down with my arms at the side and count my deep breaths up to three. Then I continue to bounce and swing my arms left to right. Doing the same count with my breath, and then my arms go out in front of me with my wrists relaxed and my hands are hanging down and still bouncing for the same amount of breathing time.

Here is the order of the exercises. Spend around 2-5 minutes on each one since you only have an hour and want to do the exercises and get some meditation time towards the end. Just fill in the blanks with the name of your exercises.

- *Your Qigong Exercise* _____ (3-5 Minutes)
- *Your Qigong Exercise* _____ (3-5 Minutes)
- *Your Qigong Exercise* _____ (3-5 Minutes)
- *Your Qigong Exercise* _____ (3-5 Minutes)
- *Your Qigong Exercise* _____ (3-5 Minutes)
- *Your Qigong Exercise* _____ (3-5 Minutes)

- *Your Qigong Exercise* _____ (3-5 Minutes)
- *Your Qigong Exercise* _____ (3-5 Minutes)
- *Your Qigong Exercise* _____ (3-5 Minutes)

With the average around 5 minutes per exercise, this should take between 40-45 minutes to complete.

Around 6:55-7:00 pm

Meditation

Since I have my music already set up before the start of class, I play a guided meditation CD. I give the students 10-15 minutes to meditate. While your Qigongers are meditating, walk around the room and do some healing. If you have others that are at your level or higher, ask them to help out if you have a large crowd. If the crowd is too big and you don't have enough time, meditate with your group.

7:10 pm

Self-Healing Exercise

By this time, it is getting towards the end of class. I go through my list of self-healing exercises that I studied. I spend a few minutes teaching the class on a particular healing technique. It may be the one on diabetes and stroking your fingers to increase or decrease sugar levels. Maybe show them the spot underneath their nose how to rub this pressure point when someone is about to faint or is having a seizure.

If you have a self-healing book (maybe something Qigong related) with over 60 methods, you'll have one healing technique a week which you'll have enough to last you more than one year. Then repeat them. Just check these off the list so you won't have any repeats during the year.

7:15 pm

End of class

Have everyone throw Qi at each other and wish everyone a wonderful day. End exactly on time to respect your student's busy schedules. Remove your sign(s), pack up, turn the lights off, lock up if need be, and have yourself a great rest of the day.

You can use this example for your own practice group or create your own. Some will do an hour and a half to two hours by extending the exercises or meditation. They may have their meditation first, then the exercises. Some groups share their experiences with Qigong. Feel free to do whatever is comfortable for you. This is good outline to begin with.

SAMPLE 90 MINUTES & TWO HOUR QIGONG PRACTICE

90 Minute Practice

5:15 pm: Class begins.

5:15- 6:10 pm: Do the Qigong Exercises.

6:10 - 6:30 pm: Meditation - During this time, walk around the room and do your healing on your Qigongers (if able to).

6:30 - 6:40 pm: Finish up any of your Qigong exercises.

6:40 - 6:45 pm: Teach a self-healing technique.

6:45 pm: *End of Class*

Two Hour Practice

6:15 pm: Class begins.

6:15- 7:15 pm: Do the Qigong Exercises.

7:15 - 7:45 pm: Meditation - During this time, walk around the room and do your healing on your Qigongers (if able to).

7:45 - 7:55 pm: Finish up any of your Qigong exercises.

7:55 - 8:00 pm: Talk about a particular Qigong exercise. Pick one exercise, explain the benefits of it, and show how to do it, get the audience involved and walk around the room. Check their posture, hand positions, breathing, etc. Make suggestions if needed to help improve their Qigong workout.

8:00 - 8:10 pm: Share stories from around the room on Qigong. Create an open forum, answer questions, or bring a list of topics to discuss on Qigong.

8:10 - 8:15 pm: Show a self-healing technique. Maybe lowering your blood pressure, lower cholesterol levels, work on sugar levels, etc.

8:15 pm: *End of class*

You can change it up to however you want. These are just examples. You may come up with your own ideas, but keep in mind the length of time it will take for each segment. Practice these yourself to make sure you are not short on time or exceeding your time limit.

A FEW WORDS ON QIGONG AND PREGNANT WOMEN

At some point in time you will have women who are pregnant. I suggest that you do not guess or ask if anyone is pregnant. Don't walk up to someone and say "How many months pregnant are you?", and then be told that they are not. This could be a very embarrassing moment for both parties. Never assume.

There are a few Qigong exercises that are not recommended for those who are pregnant. If you have any ladies in the class, you can just mention "If anyone is pregnant, this particular exercise is not recommended". If you do a Qigong overview class before people can attend your regular sessions, this should also be mentioned.

With some Qigong exercises, *reverse breathing* may be involved. When doing so we work with the lower dantian. Doing the reverse breathing while pregnant can disturb the baby. The recommendation for pregnant women is to just breathe normally.

I had several questions on pregnancy and practicing Qigong. I approached one of the Master Healers at the Qigong facility I learned from. They helped me better understand why certain exercises were not advisable during pregnancy and I would like to share them with you.

While performing Qigong, there are a some exercises that have *bouncing*. Pregnant women are discouraged from performing these bouncing activities. You can mention the alternatives to those who are carrying a child. The recommendation is to just stand or sit and wait for the next exercise, walk around the room, or meditate.

In other exercises, certain movements will not hurt the baby, but may not be peaceful to the baby. Avoid these movement. The expectant mother can just walk around the room, sit and wait, or just meditate while standing or sitting.

There are some exercises that involve heel drops and this too is not recommended. Again, make the suggestion of walking about the room or waiting for the next exercise.

Consult those who are experienced in these areas of Qigong when it comes to those who are pregnant.

Total Time in Doing the Entire Set of Exercises

Take a look at your list of exercises. Which ones will you teach for your class? Figure out how long it would take to do each exercise and add it up. What is the minimum amount of time and the maximum it would take perform those exercises? Try creating a daily routine for yourself, this doesn't mean that you have to carve out over an hour, or two and a half hours of your time each time you practice Qigong. An hour at best or longer would be great, but if you are on limited time, try 30 minutes a day. I schedule myself for an hour each day, and if things get pretty hectic, as has happened, then I shoot for 30 minutes or more if I can get it.

If you're going to teach a class, I would recommend sticking to a set of exercises and practice them all each day at home for about 45 minutes to an hour for over three months, so you get to know the routine by heart. If possible, also include a guided meditation (about 30 minutes). If 1.5 hours is too much each day, try alternating days between Qigong and a meditation. So you do Qigong exercises on one day, then the next day you do a guided meditation, then the next day the Qigong exercises again, then the next day, the meditation, etc. Just keep alternating from one day to the next. This will help put you in the mind of the student when they will be learning from you.

Once you get into a routine, your body will sense when to move onto the next exercise. With a clock on the wall, you can also better gauge yourself. So if you will be teaching a one hour class with a meditation, you can do your exercises for about 45 minutes, then 10 minutes of meditation, and 5 minutes left over for questions from the class, or teach them a self-healing technique. Customize it to whatever works best for you.

CHAPTER SIX
The First of Many Years

"Happiness is the Spiritual Experience of Living Every
Minute with Love, Grace, and Gratitude"
- Denis Waitley

This is a short chapter, but is one of the most important chapters to read. Our focus is on the future of your group. We've talked about setting goals, and building your group(s), but let's also think about your group and where it will be in the years to come. And possibly a decade from now. How far are you going to take it, and how long is this legacy of yours going to continue?

It's food for thought, but also important in getting you to think about the responsibility of running a group today, and several years from now. You will feel a lot of ownership of your group(s). There will be people coming and going over the years. You will build many relationships along the way, your reputation in the community will have grown, and your knowledge of Qigong will also have increased. So let's take a look at a few things, and hopefully it can get you to start preparing for things to come.

LOOKING BACK

Your first year is going to be a lot of fun and if done right, you can lead a very solid group. When I spoke with others who first started out, it took them a long time to get a group to be steady with attendees. For some, it can take over a year to do. Don't worry if you look back at your first year and you don't find it as successful as you wanted, but in retrospect, if it's still going on after a year, give yourself a big pat on the back. You've made it this far and that's important. You've done a fabulous job no matter how many people attend. You've worked hard, and it's very much appreciated. You've touched the lives of several people and that's what counts.

So take a look down memory lane, what were the accomplishments, and what were the failures? Failing at something is not negative, but something of great achievement if applied correctly. You never learn without failure. Making mistakes is expected, so don't beat yourself up over it. If you didn't learn from it, you didn't accomplish anything. I look at my failures as accomplishments. If I learned something, it's something of great value and it will take me to the next level. So I walk away a little smarter and a little wiser from my lessons. If you don't take the time to learn from it, you're not taking a step forward or a step back. You're at a standstill. Nothing learned, nothing gained.

So what has been successful for you and your group? Take note of what worked and what didn't. What did you learn on this path? Examine how you could have done things differently. Were the goals you set accomplished? Which ones were? Are you going to create new goals? Will you retry the ones that you could not accomplish? The ones that failed, are you going to take another shot at it again? How will you proceed after one year?

LOOKING FORWARD

What can you take from this past year and apply towards next? How will your group benefit from the new stuff you want to apply for the New Year?

Take a look at last year, see what goals you didn't accomplish, and apply them for the New Year. So if you started in July 2014, and now it's June 2015, start making your goals for your anniversary date before July. Go back to the S.M.A.R.T. goals and rewrite the ones that you did not complete, or create some new ones. How do you see your group before your next anniversary date? How will you see your group in the next 2 years? What's your game plan? After two years, are you going to start out with a new group? Are you just going to stay with one? Do you see a need in a particular area where you could start a new group?

If you have something that is working perfectly, don't fix it if it isn't broken. Continue doing what works best for your group and you. If things are not working out as well as you wanted, you may need to sit down and re-evaluate. Maybe talk to another group leader and start a dialog with them on areas that you're struggling with, don't be afraid to ask for some advice in their experience in running a successful practice group.

If you discover running a group is not for you, but you want to still participate in some capacity, maybe you can be a backup for another group leader, or participate in their group and help them out. People do have schedule changes, go on holiday, or have emergencies.

LOOKING BEYOND YOUR GROUP

So it's been several years, you've run a successful group, maybe you've become a certified instructor, and you're looking at expounding on what you have learned from all these years. What are your aspirations at this point? Where is Qigong taking you? What options do you have?

These are great questions to ask yourself. After so many years, will you continue to maintain your practice group? Will you pass it on to someone else? Will your new interest be in certifying people on different levels of Qigong? Maybe run a group, and certify others? Will you work at the Qigong center and heal people? Will you be a public speaker and go out and talk about Qigong and its benefits? There are many possibilities that are available to you.

Look around you and see if there is an area of need for Qigong. A local crisis center, a retirement community, at a college or high school? What are people looking for? How can you help them? Is volunteering an interest to you? How about working with the homeless or disabled? Should you spend some time at events to help spread the word about Qigong?

After several years some people are comfortable in just running a practice group and nothing more. There is absolutely nothing wrong with that. Others want to climb the mountain to reach the top, then discover that once they are at that peak, they want to continue climbing.

I can't predict the future for you, but you will know after working with Qigong for many years, teaching others, going through additional training and certifications, you may want to reach for the stars or just stay where you are. Everybody is different in their goals and how they want to pursue them. There is no right or wrong answers to any of these question I have put to you. You can also come up with your own to ponder. When you feel the need, just do it.

BACK TO THE DRAWING BOARD

While you are learning more about Qigong, you may find yourself going back to the manuals that you received during your training (and the DVD), and decide to go through them again. Make it a ritual to look at it every year, maybe around your anniversary date. The reason I mention this is that you can't absorb everything at once. I find myself going back, re-reading and picking up information that I missed from the first couple of times. You'll get familiar with some of the information in the book on Qigong, use it, and teach it. Then other information that you may have glossed over, you find yourself now returning to it; you discover it makes more sense now than it did back then.

When you're reading a book, the information may not make sense to you at the time. When you come back to it months or even years later and read it again, it may make perfect sense the second time around. I have some favorite books of mine on energy healing, and at the time it didn't click with me, or I missed something. Then when I gained more experience in that area, I go back to read it, the light bulb goes on, and it makes more sense to me now than it did back then. Pieces of the puzzle coming together.

So after a long period of time, take a look at your past Qigong studies. Go grab your notes, your book, or your DVD and take a little extra time to go through it and see if anything jumps out at you. I've gone back and noticed that something I used to teach, for some odd reason, I stopped incorporating. It could have been a change in location of the group, a new group, or change in people that may have contributed to my forgetting something. I must have been out of my element because I realized later – hey, I forgot to start out with my left side, put the tongue on the roof of my mouth, or tell people to have the pillar of light start from the top of their head to the bottom of their torso. Whatever it is, I start using it again. No worries, it happens to the best of us.

There is a lot of information to remember. I've noticed that when I close down one group and start another several months later, I have to go back to the drawing board and re-learn a few things. You'll pick it up quickly. Just play the DVD (if one's available), practice before your new group starts, review your notes, and it will all come back to you again.

CHAPTER SEVEN
Group Leader Interviews

*"You Cannot Travel the Path Until You
Have Become the Path Itself"*
– Buddha

I thought it would be great to hear stories from other practice group leaders and have them share their experiences. I found four wonderful people that I interviewed to learn more about them and their practice groups.

BARB PALMER

The story behind how my interest sparked in Qigong was during the time I was at Pathways in Minneapolis, Minnesota (USA). There were different types of classes being offered, and I knew nothing about the benefits of Qigong in any form that was being taught, so I took whatever was available to grow my knowledge around it. During my time there, I met Barb Palmer. She was one of the instructors that was teaching Spring Forest Qigong, and while taking her weekly class, I began to take an interest in the style she was teaching.

Barb also works at the Spring Forest Qigong Wellness Center with Master Chunyi Lin and has been studying and practicing Qigong for almost two decades. She is a Certified Level One and Two Instructor and Master Healer. Along with running a practice group at Pathways (a non-profit health crisis center in Minneapolis), she teaches classes at the local colleges on the subject of Qigong.

She gives individual healing sessions, is a public speaker, produces and facilitates workshops, participates at conferences and other events, and lives in the Twin Cities.

I decided to catch up with Barb while I was visiting my family in Minnesota at the time, and share her story with you.

Since I knew Barb, she always had this high energy about her, but also a calming effect and peaceful. Someone who is gentle, loving, and caring. The perfect ingredients for someone who is deeply involved with Qigong. As we sat down, I wanted to get to know a little more about the person who was my first instructor in Qigong. I asked Barb what sparked her interest in learning it. With a smile on her face, and seeing the look in her eyes as she traveled back in time, you could see many great memories were flooding through her mind.

Jim: When and where did you start your Qigong practice Group?

Barb: I was in a practice group which started in 2000. There were 6-7 of us in the group, and we decided that we wanted to help other people. So Pathways (in Minneapolis, MN) came to mind. Since they worked with those who have crises' (physically, emotionally, mentally, and spiritually) we asked them if we could teach Spring Forest Qigong as it would complement the audience they were helping.

We also had a conversation with Master Lin to let him know about Pathways and that we had a strong interest in teaching there. He was very happy to see Spring Forest Qigong being offered there, that many people would benefit from it.

We were the first providers at Pathways to be a "group provider". We began teaching in 2001/2002. We had a group of people, we would have 1-2 people be the presenters, and the rest of us would help out. We had an overview (a two hour class) giving all the information about the exercises, and the meditation, and we would condense the information about what Qigong and energy is, but mainly focused on the exercises.

The overview was so helpful, that people wanted more. So that is why I decided to start my own practice group there. It was 2002 that we started doing the overviews and then based on the demands by people at Pathways, I started my own practice group in 2002. At that time I was doing a weekly practice group during the days at Pathways.

Jim: Can you share with us some examples of the difficulties that you encountered in starting your own practice group?

Barb: *It was hard to draw the people because back then, Qigong wasn't widely recognized. We were only doing the overview classes once a month at Pathways. So I was mainly drawing on people from the overview classes. The classes were in the evening, and it was even harder to get people to come during the day time because people were working, and they could not make it.*

In the very beginning it was hard to get people, I would only get 1 or 2 that would show up. The word got out by Pathways, they did the marketing, since they advertised the group every month in their calendar. So it did take a while, but the group did grow to about 5-6 people regularly. After several years, we started doing the overviews in the afternoon, which drew more people who were available at that time. Then we started getting more people in the practice group.

Initially, we committed to one year and had seven people. After that, four people dropped out, leaving three of us committed to teaching the overviews at Pathways. I look back now and it seems like just yesterday that we started. Now it's been 12 years. That's a long time. Thinking back, I would have changed a few things.

I think what I would do differently is to try to have the people interest their friends and family to come to Pathways. I know there wasn't a lot of people coming, in the very beginning. If I did some sort of spreading of the word, or maybe if there was some way to market it more, it would have grown the group a lot easier.

Jim: Barb, if one of your students that was practicing at your sessions wanted to go through the training to start their own practice group, what advice would you give to them before they start teaching on their own?

Barb: *I would advise them to go through level one, take the full course, make sure they feel comfortable doing the exercises, and to feel that passion that they want to share it with others.*

I think that's the most important since it's coming from the heart. It's also important that they feel comfortable in the exercises. The main thing that they should have is the passion for the Qigong.

Jim: For those who have started a Qigong practice group, you may have to deal with nervousness. Some people have difficulty speaking in front of an audience. What did you do to overcome this when running a practice group for the very first time?

Barb: The very first overview I presented, well, I was a little nervous. I don't think I was ever nervous doing the practice group since I was doing the overview for a while before doing a practice group. Doing the overview presentation was very helpful for me since it helped me get over my stage fright. Because most people when they give their first class are very nervous, and it's hard to settle down. Master Chunyi Lin once talked about when you are nervous, it's really your ego, and we are focusing on ourselves.

What is a very helpful way to calm yourself, is to do the Qigong breathing, focus on your heart, focus on how much you love other people, and how much you want to help others. It helps calm you down. It really takes the focus away from yourself (ego).

Jim: What tips would you give to those on their first day of instructing?

Barb: I would say arrive at your class early, and get everything set up, make sure your music is working, and get the chairs in place. Then sit and do some meditation, or some exercises on your own. Calm yourself down. Focus on your heart. Focus on your love of Qigong. Focus your love on the people that are coming, and how much you want to share with those people.

Jim: While we chatted about Qigong, the topic of marketing the group came up. So I was very interested in what methods were being used to attract people, and what methods were unsuccessful since Barb was teaching at a crisis center. So I asked how she was getting the word out.

Barb: There was no marketing on my part, it was all done through Pathways. To get the word out on my end, I basically did word-of-mouth with people when I talked to them. I did this only if they expressed an interest in Qigong, and then directed them to the website, and the calendar online. Pathways also puts their calendar at hospitals, doctor offices, etc., which also helped in getting to a larger market of people, which also brought more people to the practice group.

Jim: We talked about professions and Barb mentioned that she was a professional volunteer, and she was also teaching classes at the local college. I asked her about the classes she taught.

Barb: *I teach classes through adult learning education with several school districts, and also private workshops. I also teach a 3 credit class, Intro to Qigong, at Anoka-Ramsey Community College. They have a 2 year integrated health and wellness degree, and so I have taught Qigong there for two semesters. It's an alternative course, and they offer it once every two years.*

It was one of the most interesting classes that I had to put together. It was a 14 week class, and I had to break everything down from the information in each of the levels (1, 2, and part of 3 of the Spring Forest Qigong certification levels) to create the class.

The college set it up for what criteria would be taught. Then I put together the content, taught, tested and graded the students. I also gave quizzes and a final test. The students would also do demos, have them do healings on each other (watched and graded), do weekly journaling with minimum number of words (which was graded).

Jim: Getting to know your audience is very important. Also finding out what is on their minds, and what kind of experience they are having – this is key to knowing your group. So I asked the question on what kind of feedback Barb was getting from her students when they practiced Qigong. What kind of results were they experiencing?

Barb: *A few students really benefited by Qigong, they were committed, and coming back every week and practicing on their own. One lady came in with a cane. She was in a car accident, she had nerve damage, so she had a lot of issues with walking and standing. You could see she had much pain and nerve problems in general.*

She came for quite a few years and it was so fun to watch her change over the months. Then one day she did not show up with her cane. Before, she could not do the seven steps of new life, but now, she can do it without the cane. She walks perfectly, and can lift her leg up now. She can walk on her own. She is now leading a practice group in the evening at Pathways.

It was very rewarding to have someone come in and become so enthused about Qigong, and then over the years, she turned into a practice group leader.

There was another fellow who had lung issues. It looked like it was seasonal, it was in the summer and winter - you could see he had lung problems. He was able to correct that. A lot of people have come in with a lot of different things. People come and go, stay one year and leave or others are there for a shorter period of time. There is an ebb and flow, but more so at Pathways since it is a crisis center. I am sure there are ebb and flows with other practice groups also.

Jim: So looking back at all the hours you have spent doing Qigong, what is the biggest impact that it has had on you?

Barb: *It has helped me to open my heart, which was the main thing.*

Jim: We have all made mistakes while teaching Qigong, and with making mistakes we learn from them. So tell me, what can you share about when making mistakes while teaching?

Barb: *It's good better or best, and you always want to do your best. You may not have the answer when someone asks you a question, so don't make an answer up, tell them you don't know and you'll get back to them. There is so much to know and I don't know everything. If asked how to heal a very rare disease, I know what I would do in that situation, but it may be different than Master Lin.*

I know in the beginning, if I was not sure of an answer, I would always tell them that I am not sure, but I would find the answer. Don't make things up. You also get medical questions, when I am not sure of an answer, I tell them, but I still try and find the answer for them.

Jim: With the great wisdom you have obtained in teaching, are there any tips you would like to share with others about Qigong and or your practice group?

Barb: *It really works. It's really hard for people who start in* *a practice group to see the benefits if they don't feel something. I think it's important to encourage people. A lot of people will feel tingling, or heat in the hands, if not right away, they will feel it within the first few months of practicing. There are those who don't feel anything at all when they practice. Those are the people who are harder to encourage, if they don't feel anything when they do the practice, they don't feel that they are shifting in any way. If they have health issues, and don't see any changes, it is hard to keep them motivated. My advice to them, pay attention to what's going on with them. Changes happen and they don't really notice it, they are subtle changes. Others notice changes right away.*

Subtle changes could be calmness, more peaceful, feeling happier, you notice that you are not reacting to situations the same way as you would have in the past. Just little things that people seem to not recognize, and so they think that Qigong is not working for them. Others around them may recognize the changes. That's when people stop to think about it when other people make a comment to them.

Jim: As you know, people have very busy lifestyles....How often do you practice Qigong, and what is the best time of day do you recommend to people who practice on their own?

Barb: *I practice every day. It may not be the active exercises, but I will do something Qigong related. That's another thing I would like to say. People think that they have to do the active exercises in order to practice Qigong every day. That's really not true. You can just do a quick 5-10 minutes sitting meditation, you can just pick out a couple of Qigong exercises, and if in the car (at the stop lights), for myself I like to do some hand massaging, or some face massaging, or even cupping my arms.*

Just do little things that can help you open up your energy channels throughout the day. So really, there is no excuse not to practice.

Master Chunyi Lin always says that you can do Qigong 24x7, just set the intention and run the energy. Or if you're having a conversation with someone, run the small universe while you are talking. If they can set up a schedule, that will make it easier. I know someone who will not leave their bedroom in the morning until she does 10 minutes of Qigong.

Or do 10 minutes before you go to bed. Basically do some of what I was talking about when you're in the car or even if you're in line at the grocery store. You can always do the active exercises in your mind and just don't do the movements. I do the breathing all the time. It is very good when people are starting qigong that they take time to do the active exercises. Especially for those who have physical health issues.

Jim: Some of us have rules when we run our practice sessions, what rules, if any, do you have for your students while attending?

Barb: *My groups unruly (with a big smile). Actually, there are no rules that are in place. Some do come late and that's okay, it's a Pathways policy and they are open to everyone. It's hard to find parking due to the small parking lot, so some people can be 5-10 minutes late because of the lack of parking. I have a tendency to always start on time no matter who is there or not there.*

During the first 5 -10 minutes, people are still coming in. Once in a while, somebody will come halfway through and just do the sitting meditation. I know some practitioners at Pathways say no admittance after the door is closed. Based on the fact that it's hard to find parking, and a lot of people have health challenges and issues, I don't really have any rules.

Jim: Since you have been doing this for a while, what advice of inspiration would you like to share with our readers on their journey in learning Qigong?

Barb: *I would say that it works, and it's a simple effective tool that can help you with any challenges you have, whether it be physically, mentally, emotionally, or spiritually. You just have to be patient with yourself as you practice and just be motivated to do the practice.*

Or I should say - Motivate yourself to do the practice. As you continue in your practice, you will see changes in yourself.

Jim: Having an organized practice group like yours, take me through the agenda of your class. Do you start out with a meditation, or go straight into the exercises first? What is your format?

Barb: *Because of the group of people that Pathways services, we like to keep our practice group shorter. Our group is only one hour. I don't do a lot of things that other groups do. I start at 1 pm, I'll take a minute or two to share anything (if I have something), then we start right away with the bouncing, and go right into the active exercises. Then about 1:30 we do the sitting meditation, and we do that for 23 minutes, then do the Harvesting of Qi after that. Then we end with hugs.*

In the beginning, if I have anything to share, I'll spend a few minutes at the beginning or at the end of the session. After the session, participants can stay and share with each other. I always stay afterwards, answer any questions and talk to everyone. I know of other groups that will do more sharing with the individual members of their experiences. Some people will have time to do actual healings on each other. We only have an hour in our group. The participants really enjoy this format.

ARDA OZDEMIR

I was referred to Arda by Tom Rogers, the President and CEO of the Qigong Institute in California. When I spoke with Arda, we had a very interesting conversation about Qigong, and I noticed that we had some similarities in how we present to our students and the ways we had marketed our groups.

Arda is a personal transformation coach, an author and speaker. He also came from the corporate world in Silicon Valley, where he was a finance executive. Many of us who have had the opportunity to work for these entities understand such an environment can be very stressful and at times can be very toxic. This toxicity can have a grave impact on mind, body, and spirit. In 2008, after healing himself from his physical, mental and emotional distress, resulting from his 20 years in corporate, he has helped hundreds of people to discover their authenticity and connecting people with their full potential.

During my conversation with Arda, I found him a very interesting person. Some of his philosophies made me really think about the way I have been teaching Qigong. I also learned that after completing his research and studies on the human psyche, he published his book in 2014 called "The Seeker's Manual". A book about the self-realization journey, how to bring change into your life and achieve your highest potential to live a joyful and fulfilling life.

Jim: At what moment in time did you become interested in teaching Qigong to a group of people? What inspired you to do so?

Arda: I used to be in the corporate world for over 20 years in finance. When I was feeling really bad, health wise, I noticed that I was deteriorating physically along with my wellbeing, so I started to hunt for remedies. Then I found Qigong. It was so powerful; it healed my sinus infection and the chronic pains I had in my body. While being in finance and seeing my colleagues around me suffering, I felt the need to share this jewel with these people. That's when I started thinking about teaching Qigong. My teacher, Master Zhao, in Freemont California, teaches "no movement" (very little movement), but mostly teaches about the stimulation of the life force energy through the dantian and other positions. So I started to teach in April 2011. Around this time, this is when I left the company.

Jim: When you first started your practice group, what were some of the difficulties you encountered?

Arda: My teaching practice was a different style than other people were teaching. What I learned is not an explicit style of Qigong, but I was getting people who wanted to have a specific style. Therefore, the first couple of sessions, I would attract five to six people then later it would go down to one or two. That's how I started experiencing this awareness in connecting with people. I had an interesting period during those times. I just told myself that I wouldn't stop, but I kept going.

The first element I learned with running a class was consistency. I tell myself that I am going to do Wednesday night and that I am just going to be there. And if no one shows up, I'll do my own routine and I will dedicate that time to do an hour of meditation or Qigong. If people do show up, I will work with them. So that was one moment that I felt the shift in my energy.

The second element.... I would say to myself, Am I supposed to teach this or teach that? That's what I felt inside, this internal struggle, but instead I should have been listening to my heart?

People were not showing up and I would think to myself that maybe I am doing something that is not me.

People wanted a certain class out of me and I tailored it too much for them. So I decided that I wanted to stick with what came from my heart in my teachings instead. So I started adjusting my classes a bit to what I enjoyed.

Jim: What happened when you made that adjustment that you just spoke about?

Arda: *I now attract around 15 people per class on average. Last class I just taught had 23 people. I decided to do some different energy practices last week and I had more attendance. It's what I enjoy and it's my true essence. I put originality into my classes. It's different than other practitioners who have a master or a teacher that they follow. Sometimes you have to follow that master's program and you have to use their form. You have no freedom or flexibility. I was struggling with this. I had formal training, but I also wanted to add my unique essence into the class. When I became comfortable with that, then everything started to flow.*

Jim: What would you have changed from what you know now?

Arda: *I learned a lot about myself over time, and knowing this, I would have implemented those changes earlier. I would have let the attachment go and not be focused on how many people would show rather than what I enjoy in teaching. Some of us just want to teach, but we want to get validation from the number of those that attend our classes. It's a different focus. One that works.*

Jim: A student of yours wants to start their own Qigong practice group. What advice would you give to them before they start teaching on their own?

Arda: *The confidence needs to be there. Whatever makes them feel comfortable, they should start with a small group, or family members, or visualize themselves teaching. And then go inward. Feel that energy within yourself and then bring it out. If you don't feel ready, forcing (the energy) it creates a lot of resistance in your flow.*

Jim: Go back to the very first day of teaching a Qigong class.

Were you nervous? What thoughts were going through your head at the time?

Arda: I was very nervous. Then I am asking myself if they are getting it and whether I was a good teacher. All this makes you nervous, and when you're nervous your energy stops flowing. We have to gain experience in being nervous. We have to be nervous initially to get through difficult times. Today when I am in my element and the energy is flowing, I don't need to do anything. People will be sitting there with you and you will see some people with tears in their eyes. This is because the energy is flowing through the room, through you, and through them.

So the Qigong element on top of it makes it so much more powerful. Nervousness is a way to get your lack of confidence and outward attention worked on.

Jim: What tips would you give to those on their first day of instructing if they are nervous?

Arda: Ground yourself. Mediate before. Do the most powerful meditation you know before you go in there. Ground yourself before you step onto the floor. Focus your attention inward on what you are teaching.

Jim: How did you market your group? What techniques have you used to attract people? What means were not so successful?

Arda: I'll start with the unsuccessful attempts first. Sending fliers out was not that good of an idea. Printing fliers and leaving them with certain practitioners also did not work. What did work for me was having a Qigong healing energy practice. My master taught me how to energetically heal with my Qigong methods. So I was using that as a promotion to my meditation classes. I also taught individual sessions on Qigong. When someone came to a session, I would charge $30. While I was teaching them Qigong and meditation in these individual sessions I would inform them that I was forming a weekly Qigong class and would ask them to come by and check it out. Towards the end of the first year, everything was starting to come together.

I also have a Meetup group on the Internet with 500 people, but not all of them show up or subscribe to my emails. I have accumulated a good amount of people who come one or two times a week, one or two times a month, or attend every other month.

This type of online marketing that I use helps with attendance. The other type of marketing I do are newsletters about Qigong and energy. I have over 750 people on my email list that I keep informed about my classes.

Going back to the Meetup.com groups, what I discovered is that members sign up and tune out. People don't want to get a lot of emails, but Meetup keeps emailing the members constantly. "How was the class?" "Rate the class." "Stay in touch." Or "There is another class coming up". When people get these, they don't want to get bombarded with emails. Sometimes members turn off their email notifications. So with these frequent announcements, people tune out and you get a small percentage showing up to your group.

Jim: Since you left corporate, what are you doing full time?

Arda: *I have the healing practice. It's called "Qigong for Balance". This is where Reiki and Qigong healings are performed.*

Jim: What feedback have you gotten from your students when they practice Qigong? Have they shared any of their experiences with Qigong?

Arda: *It's transformative. Qigong is so powerful. If they do it regularly they see changes, even after classes. It doesn't work on everyone, but when someone is open to it, it can be very transformative. One feedback I have gotten from a person was that from a single session it changed them. They moped around before and now they can see what's happening more in their life. They feel empowerment, clarity, and a sense of knowing of where they are going. I have gotten some beautiful responses from people over the years.*

Jim: Looking at all the hours you have spent doing Qigong, what is the biggest impact that it has had on you?

Arda: *I feel very healthy. I feel like I am in the flow almost all the time with my highest potential. That's what Qigong gave me. If I don't do my Qigong practice in the morning, I feel naked all day and vulnerable. I feel that I am not living my highest potential for that day.*

Jim: We've all made mistakes while teaching. Share with us your experience making those mistakes while teaching Qigong?

Arda: Make those mistakes. Accept that you can. The pressure I put on myself brought my energy down and made me more nervous. Today, if I make a mistake or forget something, I don't really dwell on it. I go back to the present moment. It's in the past, and I come to the moment of teaching and move on. That's what Qigong teaches us. Go with the energy, go with the flow.

Jim: With the great knowledge you've obtained from teaching over the years, any word of advice that you would like to share with others about Qigong, your practice group, or both?

Arda: I think every Qigong teacher should be an example. Be unique in what you do. I understand that there are traditions, but everybody can bring an inner wisdom and share with others. I would focus on that. I would highly recommend people to focus on their individuality. Then maybe there is a reason why you forgot a movement, or something didn't resonate with you. Maybe you didn't feel the value of it in your practice. Maybe when you were doing a certain practice and your hand went a little further and you noticed some tingling on the bottom of your feet. You did something different and there were some results. Bring that experience into the class, it's part of your uniqueness and individuality. And the other thing is focus. Live by it.

Jim: What kind of experiences have you had since you started Qigong?

Arda: The opening. The opportunities coming into my life, things that I have never imagined before. Life became so beautiful. The beautiful scenery around me. The energy going up. The delight becomes so wonderful. I feel more grounded and more connected. My head is much clearer and I have much better health.

Jim: With people having busy lives, what is the best time of day do you recommend to practice on your own and how often do you practice Qigong?

Arda: I practice every day and I would recommend others to practice right after they wake up. There is less interruptions (like cell phone distractions) and the energy is better in the morning since you feel better throughout the day.

Jim: What are the ages of those who attend your class? Can you also share with us the occupations of these people?

Arda: *It varies. I get people from the ages of 25 to 65. In my area, many people are high tech. I have a corporate background and I noticed that they have a greater trust in me. There are also engineers, managers, lawyers and accountants. Some are moms, gardeners, those learning martial arts and connecting with the earth. There is a big mix of occupations.*

Jim: What is the number of people that have attended your group? Do you have a minimum amount of people attending before you would teach?

Arda: *Smallest size I've had was around one to two people. The largest so far has grown to 23 people. There is no minimum amount for me to teach.*

Jim: What rules do you have for students while attending your sessions?

Arda: *I ask that my students be opened minded and be present.*

Jim: Looking back to the days when you first had an interest in teaching Qigong, what did you do to get your own place for your group?

Arda: *I met someone and they were renting this space, and I asked if I could teach a class on an hourly basis. They said yes at a rate of $15 per class. Then I put a sign on the door the days I teach.*

Jim: When someone is interested in teaching their own Qigong practice group, what advice would you give them in trying to find a venue?

Arda: *Go to the community centers, churches, yoga studios, and just open your eyes. The door is there. Just walk in. I was offered a space after I did that. Try looking for a place that offers classes.*

Jim: Do you practice any other exercises? Like Yoga, Tai-Chi, or practice a martial art to help build your mind, body, and soul?

Arda: *I do yoga and some Tai Chi (but not full form). I also do warm up and breathing exercises that I do in the morning. I spend 15 – 30 minutes every morning. I feel that since I am getting up early enough, that I plan on increasing the time.*

Jim: What advice of inspiration would you like to share with our readers on their journey on learning Qigong?

Arda: Enjoy the Journey!! If it gets too convoluted, complicated, too demanding or burdensome, then stop. Don't do it. Recollect, ground and center yourself. Then go back and try again.

Jim: What keeps your motivation going for Qigong? What do you get out of it?

Arda: Pure joy and fulfillment. Teaching and seeing others transform is such an enjoyment.

Jim: Imagine you had a time machine and you could travel into the future to visit yourself, where would you see yourself with Qigong in 10 years from now?

Arda: I still see myself practicing Qigong, but more diligently. Then I see what opportunities are being provided to me and enjoy that moment. I don't see anything specific, just me practicing and embracing it along the way.

Jim: Take me through the agenda of your class. What do you do during your class? What is the format you use?

Arda: I start with a meditation. Sometimes a breathing exercise to bring people's mind to a calmer state with a meditation of either guided or focused. Then we start warming up the body and move onto some movements to open up the energy. Once the energy is going, you can feel it in the room. Then I go into a standing meditation. When I am finishing I go into opening the dantian area and let people connect to their higher energy, that higher vibration. I don't ask people's experiences. I just open up for questions at the end but people don't share anything and I don't go through the class asking. My class is one hour long.

GADU DOUSHIN

I was first introduced to Gadu by someone over the Internet, I was looking for people to share their experiences with Qigong, and also learn about their practice groups. I met with him at his house in Minneapolis, little did I know, Gadu was originally from Japan. While talking with him and learning about his travels, this brought back that nostalgic feeling when I used to live in Japan years back.

Back in the day, I was once immersed in the culture, the language, and had traveled throughout Japan and visited many beautiful places. Emperor Hirohito was even my neighbor at one point in time, when I lived across the street from the winter palace. So it was a great pleasure to meet someone from my old stomping grounds.

While meeting with Gadu, I discovered he had a very interesting background, along with having some very Zen like characteristics. He is a Subbody Butoh Midwife Instructor, a Tao Shiatsu Level 1 practitioner, a Spring Forest Certified Instructor / Level one Master Healer, and has a Bachelor's degree in Aerospace Engineering and Mechanics. With all that, one of his life goals is to help others to heal. Along with learning the arts, he is also teaching which included workshops in the metropolitan area. Over a cup of tea and some rice crackers, we talked about Qigong and his experiences.

Jim: Gadu, about what moment in time were you inspired to teach Qigong to a group of people?

Gadu: As I was taking more classes on Qigong, it became apparent that I just wanted to share what I learned, so I took the path of wanting to become a certified instructor. I became a Certified Instructor in 2010. I lived in India for a couple of years and when I came back to the USA, I decided to teach. What really inspired me, well it was that Qigong was such an amazing thing. I mean it was so simple, and very effective. I felt like anyone could do it.

Compared to other forms of modalities that are good for the body (like yoga for example), it is sometimes hard to start and continue those modalities due to a person's physical requirements. SFQ doesn't have that. Anyone can do it. At any time, they can start in any condition. That was the reason why I was inspired to teach.

Jim: What have you learned now, compared to what you learned during the first says of learning Qigong. What would you have changed back then from what you know now?

Gadu: Before starting my practice group here in the US, I was living in India, where I was already guiding a practice group. I already had some experience with what works for people, so I wouldn't say that I would change much. In the future, I would like to do some other stuff. I would like to incorporate more of a Qi-sagge into my practice group, because my group does not require any experience, and there is always someone new every week.

So in some ways it's good, but in other ways, there is so much I can do to teach in one setting. As I go along with running my practice group, I will create some extra time for people who like to practice healing. I would like to incorporate some of this in the near future.

Jim: We sometimes are approached by people who have a passion to teach others. If you knew of someone that wanted to teach others about Qigong, what words of wisdom would you pass along to them before their first day of starting their own group?

Gadu: Just keep it simple and take it slow. I was visiting practice groups before, and some groups try to cram everything into an hour and a half. Everything just got diluted and the

information presented got lost. Instead, it's nice to do a few of the active exercises, but do it a little bit longer and maybe not to try and do too much at one time.

Jim: Someone like you who has traveled and lived in several countries, from what you've learned through your journey, and the experiences you have obtained through Qigong, what tips would you give to our readers when teaching their practice groups?

Gadu: *I think people get nervous when they feel like they have to do it themselves. There is a Buddhist concept called Tariki (reliance outside of oneself) and Jiriki (your own self effort, your own strength). When you let go your self-effort (Jiriki), other forces will come and help you. That's the concept of Tariki. Instead of trying to do it like I have to do it, that is part of your ego (I want to do it/I have to do it). Just back off and let that other force take care of things, and that will make things easier and go a lot smoother.*

Jim: We all need to get the word out and we use different methods in marketing our groups, what methods have you used to attract people? Share with us your successes in this area.

Gadu: *Marketing is a very difficult thing. It's really hard to say what is successful or not. For example, I have used a social website called meetup.com, so far I have maybe 12 people signed up in that group, but maybe 3-4 people will show up out of the 12. It is something that takes time. So whatever you use, it has to be there for a while so that it becomes visible. People also sign up, but maybe not show up.*

Sometimes people come once and then don't show up again. The best way that I have learned is not to just say that this won't work, but every effort you do, there is at least one person coming from whatever you do. So it's worth it. And that one person is worth it since they may stay and become a core part of your practice group.

Jim: I understand that you are a professional performer. What is that profession and how do you incorporate it into your Qigong?

Gadu: *I am a professional dancer, and give shiatsu (Japanese Massage, kind of like acupuncture, but use of hands instead of needles). As a dancer, those people I work with, they know I do Qigong. The kind of dance I do is Butoh. It is all sort of* *connected to Qigong. And my shiatsu practice is also really connected to it spirituality. In reality, all three of these things are all connected. I introduce some of the Qigong into my Butoh classes, and also bring some of my shiatsu knowledge to the practice group. It's all very interchangeable. Some of the dancers from Butoh visit and do Qigong in my group. Some people from my practice group will come out and receive shiatsu, and some dancers show up once in a while. Butoh is like a movement meditation, so Qigong has been helpful in getting into Butoh faster.*

Jim: As we run our groups, we get comments from our students since over time they are seeing changes. What have you heard from your students when they practice Qigong?

Gadu: Some people can sleep better, in general, a few have a lot less pain issues, physical issues, and it seems like it works for them. An obese person after coming to Qigong classes changed their routine and added physical exercises, trying to take care of themselves more. A couple of people who came with depression, after 3-4 session they started smiling.

People come back, so this means something. Especially those who have not studied with Qigong yet. I do not do an overview, I just give simple explanations before they start. But if people want to know a deeper understanding of Qigong, the background, the process and the philosophy behind it, I teach the level one class once in a while. For the practice group, I felt that it is better for people to get the experiential basis than knowledge basis.

Jim: From all the hours you have spent practicing Qigong, what is the biggest impact it has had on you?

Gadu: It all started with my Butoh practice. I was doing a different type of dance before, but decided that I wanted to study Butoh. It originated in Japan and unfortunately there's no schools in Japan to teach this dance. I wanted to study it intensely, and I found a school in India where a Japanese man had started teaching.

I was there in 2007 for 6 months, and after I came back to the US, I felt I was spiritually disconnected. It was a big culture shock coming back here. That's how I started studying shiatsu. This particular shiatsu is called Tao Shiatsu. It was very connected to Buddhism and spirituality. Along the way I also found Qigong and I really liked how it complemented the rest of the things I was involved with. My life has changed so much in the past 5 years. It is hard to say what one particular thing had an impact, but it seems everything is better. I have been doing Qigong since 2008.

Jim: We are all human after all and at times we make mistakes while we teach others. What are your thoughts in this area of making mistakes while teaching Qigong?

Gadu: People can make mistakes by saying that they know something when they don't. People ask really difficult questions, especially in the level one class. Sometimes I say I don't know. I will seek answers from Spring Forest and then get back to my student. I think that the biggest mistake you can make is that you say something when you actually don't know if it is true or not. It's easy to think that you understand something when you don't.

A friend of mine was not interested in taking SFQ, because the things she heard from someone else (about how they practice), she felt that something was not right about it. She started coming back because I talked to her. I believe that it was some kind of misinformation or misunderstanding. It's easy to interpret what you learn, and when you do, there is always that risk of miscommunicating.

That's why I think that it is very important to stick with the simple stuff. Because everyone has a different background in whatever they learn and sometimes it is easy to combine all that different knowledge into one thing. There is something good about that, but if you are just doing Qigong, simply do Qigong, I think that it makes it a lot easier.

Missing an exercise doesn't matter while teaching. When I first started, I forgot the name of joining Yin and Yang, oh man, I had to look it up. What was the name of that exercise (laughing to himself)? It's okay. It's good, better or best. It's the same for practicing and the same for teaching too. This whole idea of having to be perfect, it is completely opposite of what Qigong is all about.

Jim: As you know, there is a lot involved with running a Qigong practice group. So what words of wisdom would you like to share to help others become successful in running their own practice group?

Gadu: I don't know what other people do, but I go out and visit other practice groups to see what they do. What really helped me start my practice group and keep it going was at the world conference (International conference), there was a practice group leader meeting before the conference started. I couldn't afford to go to the conference, but I went to the meeting in the middle of a crazy snow storm, which I am glad I did since there was people from all over world that I met. With this meeting of practice group leaders, what they said was really helpful.

Networking and learning from other practice groups and their leaders are very useful things. If you're going to start your own practice group, you should attend one of them. The guild meetings are also kind of like a practice group. You can learn from them in how to do the exercises.

So my advice is to do the exercises. This is how I learned and it also helped me in knowing what I wanted to do in my practice group.

Jim: Since you've been practicing Qigong for a while, what changes have you noticed within yourself?

Gadu: You start noticing things a lot more, like more awareness of your surroundings, I have also noticed that good things just happen. It's not like good things come to you. Doing this kind of practice, you tune yourself to walk the path, so that you go towards the good things. It feels like good things come to you, but you just go that way. Some things are not so good in a way they are happening, it doesn't feel like some kind of burden, but it feels like it's some sort of opportunity. Its perspective. Your perception changes about everything.

Jim: How often do you practice Qigong and what would you recommend for others?

Gadu: Every day. I do miss a day, once in a while. I was doing the 100 day practice, but didn't finish since I was traveling. I am not particularly strict like that. I remember being on a plane, it was a long flight, and wondering what would the passengers think if I started to do Qigong. If you don't have the time, you just don't have it.

When I practice, I do it the first thing in the morning. I am a morning person and when I get up, I start practicing. I practice around 4:30 am. But depending on what time I go to bed, I may do it later. I teach at night and sometimes when I come home late, I may end up practicing later in the morning. Some people have different schedules and may work at night. Some are evening people and have a hard time getting up in the morning.

Jim: What is the largest amount of people that have shown up so far to your group? What is the smallest? Do you have a minimum amount of people attending before you teach?

Gadu: *Largest so far is 8. Smallest was about two people. There is no minimum for practicing. I'll teach if even one person shows up.*

Jim: Looking back when you first had an interest in teaching Qigong, what did you do to secure your own place? What ideas came to mind of location, type of place, size of room, etc.?

Gadu: *I am already renting studio for my own Butoh teachings. In the Twin Cities, there is a lot of dance studios. I am not connected to a religious community, but I am sure there are a lot of churches, or even in their basements that are available for people to utilize. I don't know how easy it is to find the free places. I usually ask for donations if people can give to support the studio. The size of the room I teach in is around 600 square feet.*

Jim: When someone is interested in teaching their own practice group, what advice would you give them in trying to find a venue?

Gadu: *The easiest place to find is a neighborhood community center. Some charge, others are free. It is a good place to start. For me it was dance spaces. If you are around any art spaces or art collective buildings, this is another good option. When I wanted to teach Butoh, I went to the art collective buildings. I put out an ad at these places saying that I was looking for space.*

If you know of a location that you want to run your practice group, it might be a good idea to post your ad there. Also ask around. Some people know of free spaces. If you can find it for free, that's even better.

Jim: Do you practice any other exercises, like Yoga, Tai-Chi, do mediation, or practice a martial art, to help build your mind, body, and soul?

Gadu: *I do Yoga and Butoh - which is a form of Japanese dance.*

Jim: What advice of inspiration would you like to share with our readers in their journey on learning Qigong?

Gadu: *This is a kind of work when you think you know, then you really don't know. So, I think that just knowing that it is infinite, is key. Some people want to perfect the technique, but in the end, it really doesn't matter. So what's the point if it is this way or that way? If you try to grasp it with your conscious mind, it's really hard, because it's really not, that's what Tao is. If you really can't say it, it's not Tao.*

I think that's what really drove me into the place that I can keep exploring deeper, deeper, and deeper. Sometimes it gets frustrating, because you don't know where you are in the big scheme of things. But when someone like Master Lin talks about his experience, it's like - okay, I understand, but there is a lot more to it. That's probably what inspired me to keep going, there is so much infinite depth to it.

Jim: What keeps you motivated in practicing Qigong?

Gadu: *It makes me feel good. It's like a feeling of oneness, it kind of sounds corny, but that's basically what it is.*

BRUNO FRANCK

It was a great pleasure to interview Bruno. I was introduced to him by Gadu one day, and I learned during our meeting that he has been doing a lot with Qigong which goes well beyond running practice groups.

Bruno works with senior citizens and also with the homeless in teaching them the benefits of Qigong. Bruno is a level 1 Master Healer, a level 1 and 2 instructor, and volunteers at the SFQ Center, Well Within, and the Dayton's Bluff Seniors Nurse Program.

With his ongoing personal development, he teaches topics such as acupressure and Qi~ssage, anxiety, energy healing, depression, cancer, forgiveness, and issues specific to men. He also participates in ongoing teleseminars, and is a level 5 Student/practitioner of SFQ.

I visited Bruno at his home in the Twin Cities, and was greeted by his very loving dog, and a wonderful cup of tea on that very chilly Minnesota winter morning.

Jim: At what moment in time did you become interested in teaching Qigong to a group of people? What lead you down this path?

Bruno: For me, what really happened, was when I had my first exposure to Qigong, I thought to myself - what is this thing? I heard a lot about it from other people, and after receiving some gentle advice from them, I decided to check it out. When I started practicing, it was really surprising to me. What was this cause and effect with this new phenomenon? While practicing, I realized that there was something much deeper, more intuitive going on here, and this had an impact on me. That's what really intrigued me about Qigong. Plus you actually do get positive results. To learn more, you have to go out and practice. So where do I go out and do this? Well that's when I went out and followed the suggestion of joining a practice group, and started volunteering.

Jim: Can you share some insight on the difficulties you have encountered, and looking back, what advice would you give to those who are starting their own practice group?

Bruno: When the time has come to start my own, I thought to myself, where do you go? Where do I get some help? Really not knowing where to go, and with my background at the university (I am an engineer and had no medical background), I realized that Qigong was a lot about healing. Someone like me and my background, how does this all work out?

Where do I go, what credentials do I tap into? Several of my colleagues are in the medical field (a nurse, a psychologist, and others I know in this profession), and they bring Qigong to their own practice to make it available for their people.

I have some great friendships with those in Qigong, and they have helped guide me. I remember somebody would start putting together a flier and distribute it in the neighborhood, in the grocery stores, in the cafes, etc. A little brochure in their own words about Qigong. But how do you get the message across for someone doing it for the first time and for others who have practiced it? Where do I find a location that people don't have to drive so far? Can we do this in a hospital, a church, at a community center?

You'll do just fine in trying to find a place if you've never done it before. But it takes that get up and go to go out and do it. It also takes every bit of confidence, and also a lot of guts. With Qigong, you sort of keep doing it from the heart.

And also working with people that have never done this before. How do you communicate well in the beginning, so people get the right message? These are things I and others have struggled with, but I have learned that you go with your heart. This is the best direction to go when starting your first practice group, go with all your heart.

The one thing, I would actually advise that people do is be patient, patient, patient. Having a practice group may not happen in three months or six months or one year. You do end up with so much of an influence with those you work with, you need to feel very good about it. It does take time to establish your group. Place your level of ambition and deal with your own ego, and you'll start moving.

Don't look at establishing a timeframe or trying to have a specific number of weeks per month for a return, don't put too much time into the equation.

Jim: Thinking back to the first weeks, or even months, what would you have changed back then from what you know now?

Bruno: *Trust your heart. I have been teaching at the university for many years, and I enjoy being in front of a group of people. Yet, being in front of a group in Qigong, I realize that this is a much different way in how it is taught, where everyone in the class was bringing something in participation. I would ask if anyone would like to share their opinion, or like to lead this part of the group. This is exactly how it was done for me.*

It was a different experience in how it was being received by all. It's also realizing what's happening in class (the experience), that it is diverse for everyone. As a group leader, you get to experiment with your practice in how it can be taught, and everyone becomes a part of it. It's amazing how much those in the group contribute to the class.

Jim: In marketing your group, what methods have you used to attract people?

Bruno: Word of mouth with people you know or meet, bring awareness to others at meetings that you have a group, also exchange information with others and learn about theirs. Some people that are leading their own groups, they also make referrals to other group leaders.

Jim: What feedback have you gotten from your students when they practice Qigong? What kind of results have they experienced?

Bruno: It's all over the place. From those who have struggled with extreme pain (like after an organ transplant), people who are dealing with cancer, to those needing pain management. People come from all over with all sorts of ailments, and I have gotten some positive results with Qigong, and from those who have experienced it. The feedback has been wonderful since day one. Some come in once or twice a month, most with serious health problems.

Jim: Looking at all the hours you have spent doing Qigong, what is the biggest impact it has had on you?

Bruno: It's completely life changing. I do this essentially on a full time basis. I am not yet making any money from it, but have been doing this for several years, it's all volunteering, and I am in venues where people need a lot of assistance. And that is also where my heart is. That's sort of what motivates me and all at the same time that is how I am able to take care of myself. That's the one thing that took me a long time to understand.

Whatever you do, make sure you do it for the right reason. This is very important in order to take care of yourself, first and foremost, take care of yourself. You have to find a way to take care of yourself to help others so you don't burn out. The more you do it, the more energy you have. At the end of an entire day, you feel just as good as you did in the morning. At times I find myself bringing energy to the group. When you tap into it, it's amazing. When I was teaching at the university, after 12 hours of lectures, I had to take a rest. I would have a cup of coffee and go walk outside to try and clear my mind. I used to do physical exercises for the same thing, to clear the mind and try to keep the

body healthy. Qigong is for the mind, body and spirit and I learned how to integrate into my physical exercises.

I use to go like a maniac, doing those physical exercises and feeling really good about my heart. I was sweating, drinking so much water, because I was so thirsty, I would come out of it so exhausted, it would take a couple of hours for me to recover.

But I learned to integrate Qigong, the breathing, the attitude of going into my heart, and I feel good when I come out of it with less of a recovery time. I can just go out and do a full day of activities. That's what you discover over time when you do the Qigong exercises, you feel more energy than before. You sort of bring that into the teaching that you do in these practice groups. I simply just advise people to do this since it will bring more energy to them.

Jim: Bruno, let's talk about the ego. How does this and teaching Qigong come into play?

Bruno: *If you tap into your own ego, that's not going to be very easy. I don't want to bring in negatives about attitudes, in some ways that's what it is. We are all human, and we all have different reactions with all different people. When I started to lead a group, I remember a fellow that came who had a different perspective of Qigong. He was at one of the events and I was sharing my story about healing, and he started to snicker.*

Well that's going to happen and that makes it more interesting and funny. How do you teach somebody like that? He was reacting to me, and I was reacting to him. It goes both ways. The only person that I could change was not him, but it was me. This is what I am talking about, the ego. If you don't understand the ego, it can be difficult to understand awareness, so some people react as being fearful or frightened. When teaching Qigong, don't let your ego get in the way, go into that emptiness, and go into that place of pure unconditional love. Speak from the heart. Let that love lead you and not your ego.

Jim: If you could just give one tip about Qigong, what would it be?

Bruno: *Trust it and be patient. If you have the passion, just go out and do it.*

Jim: When do you practice Qigong?

Bruno: I Practice around 5-7 am. When I lead practice groups, I practice a little bit at the beginning.

Jim: What time of day do you recommend?

Bruno: It's up to the person to find out what works best for them and just do it. Just ask yourself, when is the best time of the day or when you have a few minutes to just do it? You're going to see that over time, the more you do it at the same time, the more you find the time to do it. Even if it's sometimes a little here and a little there, it's going to allow you to tap into mindfulness.

Jim: How long did it take to start your first practice group? What can you share about your groups?

Bruno: I don't remember how long it took to start my first group, but it was called the "Women Well". It was an organization that I volunteered for, one that I had to go through a criminal background check, and then I was given a venue to lead the practice group. I do remember that it took some time to establish that group.

As a group leader, I expect others to stay within the confinement of the time the class starts and ends. I always start and finish on time, and respect other people's schedules. This is one of the things that I would recommend a group leader should consider.

Personally, I like teaching, and I like being with people. So I always trust that something good is going to happen. I've learned to go with my heart mutually and somehow it happens. So if you have doubts when leading a group, go with your heart, collect the anxiety, and deal with the emotions. You will be successful in what you set out to do.

When I do a healing on a group, I do a little bit of teaching every single time. I show them how to do the sword fingers, rubbing of the hands, etc. I now find myself teaching more topics than ever before.

Jim: What are the ages of those whom attend your class?

Bruno: Middle age to elderly people. Mainly I work with the homeless, and also with senior citizens. But I have also had some young people attend.

Jim: How long have you been teaching Qigong?

Bruno: Started in 2009. Over the years, people are slowly telling me to charge for money, but I work with the homeless and want to give back to our community. Some people will give donations to help accommodate for the classes and this is greatly appreciated.

Jim: What advice of inspiration would you like to share with our readers in their journey on learning Qigong?

Bruno: Go out and do it and allow yourself to become a healer. Be confident in what you do, and become a healer so others can benefit.

Jim: Besides running your own practice groups, you also teach some classes related to Qigong. Can you give us some information on what you teach?

Bruno: Depending on the class. This week I will be talking to a group about Qigong and diabetes. In that class, I would be doing a very short talk for those who recently discovered that they have diabetes. Helping them in feeling confident, ending the stress, then doing some of the Qigong teachings. I would also advise them on doing the exercises as often as they can. Will it be a half hour, or an hour? That would be up to them. It's not part of my support group or my practice group. It's just a small group, for a small duration and on this topic.

I also do short, very brief discussion, with meditation to help people. It is used to guide them to just go deeper into their hearts, and help find out why they are here. People visit to check things out and find out what Qigong is all about. We also work with pain management. We use meditation to feel the pain, to see how negatively it is affecting our lives. There's a Buddhist way of presenting it, it's about planting words, those seed to help deal with our own pain. Learn how not to view it negatively, but instead befriend it.

JIM CORMICAN

During the time I was finishing the draft of this book I was meeting with my friend Chris on Halloween and told her about it. I mentioned the people I interviewed and the wonderful stories they had shared with me. Chris has known me for a while and she said that I should be interviewed for my own book.

I thought that something like that would be kind of strange, getting interviewed in my own book, but then I thought to myself (putting on that entrepreneur hat), and wondered if anything like this has been done before. Hmmmm.... Something unique and different? Will I be starting a trend that others will follow? I am always looking for ways to raise the bar. Would this give the wrong impression if I was interviewed in my own book? I was kind of against it, but my mentors remind me that people see me differently than I see myself, and the lives that we all touch makes in impact in one way or another, no matter how small it is.

So I thought to myself that I'll give it a shot. I asked my granddaughter to do the interview since she was available and really has a talent for such things. First I will share a little background on myself which will lead up to the interview and how I was introduced to Qigong.

I have been an entrepreneur for a long time, have created several startup companies and along the way have experienced many successes and failures. I've learned that making mistakes can bring you closer to your achievements and it doesn't have to be at that moment, but it could be years down the road from what you learned that could bring you success.

One of my favorite successes was turning a failing small entrepreneur Meetup.com group with a handful of people (along with experimenting with different ideas to grow it and making many mistakes during this time); increased its membership close to 1,000 people and eventually turned it into a business. The business networking group originated in a small cafe in south Minneapolis, then migrated to a restaurant down the road using their small party room (which we outgrew). Later on a partnership was formed with a company called CompUSA using their training rooms (yep we also outgrew that location) and then a strategic partnership was made with a multibillion dollar corporation called Best Buy, in Richfield Minnesota.

With my team, we brought over 3000 business owners to Best Buy Corporate Headquarters' front door during our partnership along with some very well-known presenters and business owners. We had people like Robert Stephens, founder of the Geek Squad, Steven Schussler, owner of Schussler Creative (founder of RainForest Café at the Mall of America), Jerry Ruzicka, president of Starkey Labs, Mark Stutrud, Founder of Summit Brewing Company, Chris Berghoff, Founder of Control Products, Sam Richter, CEO of SBR Worldwide, Scott Schwefel, Founder of Insights Twin Cities, and many other talented people who took the time to talk to our local business owners. Google some of these names, they are some of the most talented and successful people I have ever met and the stories they tell will amaze you. During this energetic time in my life, my personal network grew and grew and I became one of the most networked person in the small business world within the Twin Cities area (face-to-face, not online social websites). Things were going very well and I was on top of the world.

Then that horrible time came when the economy crashed, and like a Tsunami, the undertow was too powerful for many of us business owners to keep our doors open and it changed our lives forever. With this big influx it introduced several hardships; financially, spiritually, emotionally draining, and it hit us really hard at the homestead. With all the chaos going on, our lives felt like it was flipped upside down and the stress levels increased 10 fold. One day a friend of ours introduced us to a crisis center in Minneapolis for my wife's health and we discovered many techniques to help bring down the stressors in our lives and learned about several healing modalities. They had Qigong, Reiki, Meditation, Tai Chi, Shiatsu Massage, Energy Balancing,

Shamanic Journeying (including drumming), and many different tools that can help renew your life.

I gravitated towards Qigong and when practicing, something came alive inside me and I said to myself that I must study this, learn it and teach it to others. I was very excited about it so I took the necessary classes to teach Qigong. I got my certificates and was ready to rock and roll. Unfortunately those who taught this form of Qigong never showed people how to start a practice group. So you were pretty much on your own after the training (this is one thing that inspired me to write this book).

With ongoing life changes, I was forced to move away from my family, live in another state and work for a company that I was unfamiliar with. I decided to teach my first practice group at the Fortune 500 Company I was working for. While doing so I took notes on my successes and failures of building my practice groups. With my experience in forming business networking groups, I decided to take what I learned as an owner, a networker, an entrepreneur, a devoted Qigong practitioner and use this knowledge to start my first practice groups. Then over time I started another group at one of the local Universities and I also taught people in their homes about Qigong.

Raelyn: At what moment in time did you get interested in teaching Qigong to a group of people? What lead you down this path?

Jim: *With the many stresses in our lives, the closing of the business, my wife's health issues and not able to find employment at that time, a friend we used to work with introduced us to a non-profit organization called Pathways in Minneapolis, Minnesota. This is where the seed of Qigong was planted.*

With the many healing modalities that this organization offered, I experienced unexplainable things, like feeling an actual ball of energy between my hands during one of the Qigong exercises. It was amazing. At that moment, I wanted to explore what other things that Qigong had to offer. After several months participating in a practice group, I decided to take classes to learn Qigong so I could teach it to others. A new doorway had opened for me at this time not realizing where it would take me.

Raelyn: Can you share some insight on the difficulties you have encountered, and looking back, what advice would you give to those who are starting their own practice group?

Jim: I will talk about the corporate world, since I have lived this life for over two decades. In a corporate environment, you might think that being surrounded by hundreds or even thousands of people in a big company, you would have no problems building your group and people would be busting down the doors to learn Qigong. I discovered that this was not the case. When people see the name "Qigong" on some marketing material, they have difficulties pronouncing it. Qigong is not very well known in the West yet, but slowly growing in popularity. With a name that is unknown to people, it makes it more difficult to sell.

After getting the approval to teach I started to talk to coworkers about Qigong. When people talked about pain, I would show them a Qigong technique to help relieve their pain. Then I would inform them about my weekly practice group.

My advice is to educate your audience. This is key to sparking an interest. Invite them to a session and have them try it a few times. Over time, they will learn about the benefits of practicing and what Qigong can do for them.

Raelyn: Thinking back to the first weeks, or even months, what would you have changed then from what you know now?

Jim: I would have tried to make my Qigong practice open to the public at work so we others would join us. I think this would have made a big difference and would have changed the mindset of those people attending from the company. Get them out of their corporate mindset so they don't have that feeling that they are still at work, but with friends to increase their comfort level.

Raelyn: In marketing your group, what methods have you used to attract people?

Jim: If you try starting a group in a company, get your group added to the companies email newsletters. Companies like employees who go above and beyond and they don't mind helping them. Work with these decision makers – invite them to a couple of sessions so they can actually experience the value of Qigong. They are the gatekeepers to many employees.

When I had a group at a university, they actually did the marketing for me, but don't just rely on them, also include your own marketing. I have found that word of mouth has worked best by going in front of an audience of people. Show them Qigong. I have done lunch and learns and workshops. I have also heard a group of people talk about energy work and I told them that I had a practice group they could check out. They showed up and also informed others after taking several sessions.

I have used different methods at the same time and did not stick to just one. I look at it from a business perspective. You want different streams of revenue coming into your company and not rely on just one stream. So in marketing, you want several things working for you at the same time. It's that repetition building retention. Getting the word out can be on a blog, someone's website, or just asking friends and family members. They too can help build your practice group. They can all help in spreading the word.

Over a period of time, you will notice that a couple of "Getting the Word Out" techniques will produce more than others, and you may end up with one that just produces 1-2 people a quarter. But keep in mind that adding them all together could end up getting a dozen or more. It's not going to be instantaneous, but over time will grow.

Raelyn: What feedback have you gotten from your students when they practice Qigong? What kind of results have they experienced?

Jim: *I have gotten some very interesting comments from those with whom I have worked. I remember one gentleman that was in a wheelchair. After our session ended, his face was full of tears. He said while I was balancing his energy, he felt he was inside a box and he fought not to leave it. Then he felt it open and he eventually convinced himself to leave that confinement.*

I could see on his face that he was in a little shock as I listened to him. It was a very emotional moment for him and he did not know what to do since this was a new experience. Then he decided to turn around and wheeled himself quickly out the door. Maybe he felt embarrassed, but I haven't seen him since that day. I wish him the very best and someday I may bump into him and hear his story about that day.

I have had others say that their back problems went away, a person who experienced a stroke had feeling come back in the areas that had lost sensation. I also had a person who served in Afghanistan and was involved in a roadside bombing. Their leg was damaged and they had severe headaches since then. After multiple operations on their leg the pain still remained. After several Qigong sessions, the headaches went away and the leg pain was gone.

Raelyn: If you could just give one word about starting a Qigong practice group, what would it be?

Jim: Perseverance. Don't give up. If something is not working, sit down and take a few moments to put yourself in the shoes of your potential students. Is it the location, the time, or maybe the message that you are delivering that is not understood? If you currently have students, ask them what attracted them. Is there something missing or could be improved? Ask your students again. They can give you a suggestion that could change everything.

If no one is attending, look at where your message is being delivered and change this. I've learned that if you are passionate about something, see if you can get others to share your passion and have them help spread the word. If you need to communicate a message to the masses, get others to do the work for you. Don't do all the hard work yourself. If others have a mailing list, a bulletin board, or any other way they communicate to their target audience, see if they can deliver your message for you.

Raelyn: How long did it take to start your first practice group? What can you share about your groups?

Jim: My first practice group took a while to build. It took several months. Since it was at work, I had to put several things in place before that very first day I would teach. To bring my group into fruition, one of the top things I had to do was find out who was in charge of the health and wellness program. I was lucky to have been flown out to the corporate headquarters for training and met with the person who was the decision maker. We chatted about Qigong and she gave me a release form to hand out to students before they could join the class.

After I got her blessing I started to put things together. I decided to create a two hour presentation so people that had an interest could get an introduction to Qigong and I would let them know about the upcoming practice group. I talked with individuals, scheduled a conference room and I did my presentation. About 5 people attended my first presentation and then my class. I gave more presentations later on and more people joined.

After several months, people outside of work heard about the group and contacted me. They were not employees of the company so they could not come into the building. I connected with a local university and started a new group. I was doing two groups a week after a while.

Raelyn: What advice of inspiration would you like to share with our readers in their journey learning Qigong?

Jim: *Learn as much as you can. Even if it's not the style you have learned. Crack open a book, check out an online seminar, read the blogs, get involved. The more you learn, the more you will discover about this world of Qigong. I also enjoy hearing stories by others. They inspire me. Learning more about this mysterious Qigong keeps me going and it also helps me to educate myself on the subject so I can share with my students.*

Raelyn: Imagine you had a time machine and could travel into the future to visit yourself, where would you see yourself and Qigong in 10 years from now?

Jim: *I would still see myself teaching, writing more books, and hopefully advanced enough that I would be working under a Qigong Master. Then 10 years after that I would hopefully be a Master myself spreading Qigong around the world.*

CHAPTER EIGHT
Additional Tips for Success

"It Takes a Wise man to Learn from his Mistakes,
but an Even Wiser Man to Learn from Others"
– Zen Proverb

A CHAIR WITHOUT ARMS

Someday you will be working with people that have limitation in their mobility, with aches and pains in parts of their body where they would not be able to perform Qigong standing up. To help you better understand the difficulties that people can go through, go out and find yourself a chair and practice Qigong. Seek out a chair without arms, without wheels or swivels. You are looking for a stable chair that has no arms so you are not limited by them while you're doing the motions.

I would recommend for your group that chairs have no arm rests since this gets in the way of doing some of the exercises. You want a chair that won't roll across the floor, or spin out of control while practicing.

Pick a body part and imagine that you have problems in this area with mobility. For this example, pick your legs and pretend that you can't stand for long periods of time. Focus on not being able to move your legs, or that they don't exist. Pick an exercise and see what difficulties you may experience in performing. Now choose an arm. Maybe it can't raise to a certain level, or it cannot move whatsoever. What exercises could you perform?

These simple movements will help you get to know an audience you may work with someday who may need to sit down or have limited mobility. By sitting in a chair without arms, you will better understand the challenges they will be going through, what modifications to make to that exercise you may have to perform, and enable you to teach these changes to those with limited mobility. There are going to be some differences between sitting and standing while doing these exercises.

When you do a particular Qigong exercise, what do you notice that is different performing it in a chair or standing up? Next try another Qigong exercise, then another in the chair. Take notes of how different it is and how it feels.

Try using visual imagery and pick something else. What if you have one arm? How would you visualize this? How does it feel when you perform this? Take note and practice this. One day you may have that question and you can teach them to perform that particular exercise. You will be amazed at the results when you try this for a while, especially when you start feeling a deeper inner-self and awareness. Visualization can be very powerful.

Try practicing the Qigong exercises in a chair and take notes on how you would teach your group. Perform this for about a week or until you get comfortable with it. Once you have done this for a while, you will know exactly what to do when you instruct your students that will be sitting down. I would recommend for any Qigong sessions, make chairs available to everyone. I remember that I had limitations when I first started practicing Qigong and I would fight the pain while standing and ended up sitting in the chair. The experience was uncomfortable and I thought I wasn't getting any benefit from Qigong. I was too focused on how long I can endure the pain and not Qigong.

You want people to be comfortable while they are practicing and you don't want anyone in pain. I am glad I had a place to sit since the pain became unbearable over a period of time. It felt embarrassing at first, but I noticed others who would also follow after me and I could see in their eyes that they were grateful that someone made the first move. I guess I took away the embarrassment from others.

As a rule, always think safety when it comes to teaching your Qigongers. If a chair or the environment you are teaching in doesn't look safe, than adapt. Get a different chair, move to another room, whatever it is, you want to keep those who are around you safe and comfortable. This will provide a great experience for them all.

ASK PERMISSION

Before you touch someone in your class, ask permission first. Some people do not like to be touched, so approach your students slowly, so as not to startle them. Tell them that you want to show them something and if you need to touch their arm for example, just ask them before you do. It is polite and you are asking their permission to enter their space. The reason why this is important is that you may not know their culture or beliefs. Or they may suffer from Post-Traumatic Stress Disorder (PTSD). Respect their space and you shouldn't have any trouble. If they say no, just show them how to do it by example.

TEACHING IN SMALL TOWNS

For those that live in rural areas and want to teach Qigong, where do you begin? Depending on the population of your community, some venues you may look at are churches, at a home, out of someone's garage, a public place like a park, the library conference room, or maybe a community center. Use your imagination for finding a location. You want something that feels right for you and your participants.

Say that you've got a few friends that have an interest in learning Qigong and you are looking for a place to teach and you can't find accommodations. Start out simple and teach in your home or at a friend's place. If you can't teach in your home, consider asking someone if you can teach out of their home.

Once people feel comfortable in your group, they will start referring others and ask them to join. In small towns, almost everyone knows each other. So your group will get some advertising by word of mouth. If you are looking for some other location, try talking to your attendees. Do some social networking by announcing you are looking. You may end up at a church, a community center, or maybe a pavilion in a park. You never know until you ask. The key word is to just ask and see where things will take you.

There may be some online local groups that you could join and let others know what you are doing. Some people may also have limitations on Internet access in rural areas and may not see your group online. As I am writing this section, I live in a town of 800 people, but the community I am in probably has about 40 people or less. I didn't feel comfortable going door to door, and we really did not have any sort of social interaction between us to introduce ourselves. To help increase my comfort level, I chose to teach at work, with the company's approval.

BACKUP PRESENTATION

Sometimes you feel like the universe has thrown you a curve ball and then you think to yourself "Now what"?

If you've done presentations in the past, you may have had a situation where your projector didn't work, or it failed right in the middle of your presenting. Then everything just goes downhill from there.

Keep a copy of your presentation in paper format. I know, save the trees, but having a handout where your audience can follow would be helpful. You can just keep a stack until a time comes where you will need them. You can always request them back and ask people not to take notes on them, so you can reuse them for the next group of people in case you have another emergency. Just reuse them over and over again. You may find that a few have gone missing over time, but that's okay. Also supply people with paper and a writing utensil so they can take notes, just in case they forgot their own.

When I have created booklets to be reused, people find value in the information, and decide to keep a copy for themselves. I will reuse them for large audiences and frequent training. To get your booklets back, have them fill out a survey and ask them to turn in the booklet/presentation and survey before leaving. Now you just saved yourself some future trees in the forest so people can practice their Qigong there.

You may decide one day that you need to buy a projector. Some of them can be really expensive, plus you may need a laptop for your presentation, and this could cost you several paychecks. If you already have a smart phone, you can get an adapter to plug into the projector and share your slide show. Some projectors may even take a presentation with a USB Jump Drive by just inserting it into the USB port.

Try and be creative in this area, this can save you big money in the end.

INSURANCE

Before you start teaching your first class, you may have to be covered by some insurance, but this of course depends on the situation. For example, if you're teaching at your place of business, the company may already have insurance to cover you, but you may be required to just have those who participate sign a waiver. If you're teaching Qigong at a health and wellness center, they may not want to pay out additional insurance, so they would require instructors to cover their own costs of insuring themselves. So having a liability insurance can be helpful.

With Qigong, you do a lot of hand movements, but it's not very high impact like most exercises being offered at health clubs. So you may think to yourself, like I did, why do I need liability insurance? Every state (USA) is different, since they all have different laws. Do some more research into this to make sure that you don't end up having problems later on. It is best to cover your assets. If you are teaching outside the USA, it may be a little different due to government and culture.

When I was teaching my niece and wife in the middle of the living room of our home, my niece became very dizzy and sick and could not proceed. This could be contributed to anything and may not be related to Qigong. But if you have a student who is not feeling well, has medical issues, or medication kicking in while you are teaching and it throws them off balance, you never know where this could lead. The student may think it is contributed to Qigong since something happened while they were practicing with you, and may think doing this exercise caused them problems.

Again, just check out the local laws, talk to your insurance carrier, and do your due diligence. If you're not going solo and teaching under the umbrella of a business or an organization, have a conversation with them to see what they have done in the past. If need be, consult with an attorney if you're unsure, or if it doesn't feel right, find another place that will support you. When it doesn't feel right, or if you will be investing a lot of out of pocket money into teaching with no reimbursement (liability insurance can be US $500/year or more), find another way to teach it or walk away. If you can afford the out of pocket expense and you don't mind doing this, go for it.

When I spoke to my insurance carrier after a health and wellness center told me that I had to be insured, even when I was volunteering my time, I was quoted over $500 annually. If you are not instructor certified in Qigong, you may not be able to ask for remuneration. Some Qigong associations may ask from those at lower certified levels not charge for leading a practice group. Only those at certain levels may be allowed to charge.

If you don't have your Instructor certification to make money to cover expenses, you may be limited to specific guidelines. You will have to be creative to reach your goals. Don't let this get you down or upset you, just find another venue that is insured and can cover your class. A waiver is sometimes good enough and that's all you need (downloadable from our website).

You can also consult with other Qigong teachers that run their own practice group to see what they're doing. You may be surprised at what you find for information and support from others.

THE BACKUP PLAN – USING YOUR QI~TOOLKIT ™

You are going to run into instances where things are not going the way you expect it. Let's say you arrive late due to an accident the highway, and things are not going to well for you right now. There is already a group in the room (and they are running into overtime), and you're out in the hallway with your students waiting. What do you do? Or how about no key to the room, or there are no chairs for people to sit down, or not enough chairs to go around? Maybe you pull your CD Music collection out of your duffle bag and it is cracked - will you know how to hum a few bars of the meditation music to get people relaxed and into a meditative state?

These are some examples of what has happened to me and could happen to you. You can't prepare for everything, but having some sort of backup plan would be useful - just in case.

Here is a list of items I bring with me to help me just in case something goes wrong. Feel free to add you own. It's my Qi~Toolkit™ to help me quickly remedy the situation at hand and get back on track.

- **Handouts for Presentation:** Keep a copy, just in case your projector dies. You can hand these out and if necessary, collect them at the end of class.
- **Music:** Have a copy of your music on CD (maybe have some additional copies), and if you have an MP3 player, have a copy of your music also located on there. Having a few ways to get to your music/meditation will eliminate the possibility of not having any music or being unable to play the meditation for your practice group. Plus you will be ready for any environment for playing music.

  You can put a CD into the sound system for background music and when you do the meditation, you can quickly switch to your MP3 to start your meditation music and just power off the sound system. This saves me time so I don't have to change out CDs, especially in a CD changer that you may have to fumble around with.
- **Speakers:** I have in my duffle bag a small portable set of speakers. They are powerful enough for sound to travel across the room and it sounds really good with the frequency ranges produced by some of the music, sounds, voices, and meditations on CD. I use my smart phone (remember to put it in airplane mode so you don't receive phone calls or text messages) for my speakers. It's small, light, and portable. Test your speakers to make sure you don't get any distortion since this can create distractions or make it difficult to hear.

  I have used my speakers a few times when there is no sound system available, or the current sound system has become inoperable (or too complicated to use). I have also used both the portable and room speakers during a session. My portable speakers also have a remote control so I can adjust the volume without getting out of my chair or walking across the room. It's a time saver.

- **Surge Protector:** I have a very long cord on my surge protector that goes up to 6 feet (1.83 meters). I have used this on many occasions. It comes in handy if there are no outlets near where I am practicing. You can attach additional electrical items if needed, like your music, MP3 player, or a projector.
- **Projector:** I do have a projector as a backup, just in case the current projector does not work for my intro class. Projectors can be very expensive, so consider using the presentation handouts if this does not meet your budget. I don't carry one with me all the time, I just bring it when I know I will be teaching a class, or workshop, or if there is a projector involved. You never know when your group may put out too much energy and blow the projector bulb.
- **Batteries:** If your MP3 runs on batteries, make sure you have several spare in case you need to swap them out in a hurry. I wrap mine in tape and put the current date on them. This helps me determine later if I need to replace them. Keep these in a plastic case or baggy to protect your batteries, so they don't leak on your personal items. A zip locked plastic baggy works great. If you have a power cord, I would recommend using it, so that your batteries don't die while you are practicing.
- **Pens/Pencil/Paper:** Have some extra on hand. These can be difficult to find at a facility that you are not familiar with and you need one on the spot. If you have a sign-up sheet, you will have these on hand and available to your students.
- **Contact Information:** Make sure you always have extra handouts that have your contact information. It is a lot quicker to pass it along to someone and it looks professional. Also have a list of contacts for those who are responsible for the room so that you can quickly get a hold of them if there is a problem or emergency.
- **Erasers and Markers:** There have been a few times the markers for the whiteboards are dried up and there is no eraser to clean the board. Have a spare set with you. It is difficult to convey your message to your audience when they can't read the marker on the whiteboard. Sometimes boards are difficult to clean, so a rag and a bottle of whiteboard cleaner may also come in handy.

Sometimes the dry eraser is not enough when someone else has left their notes.

RELIGION

Religion is a very touchy subject, especially teaching a class that deals with healing. You will have your skeptics and that's okay. I expect people to be so. Everyone is entitled to their own opinions, and as a teacher; you are not here to change them, but instead be a good listener and be supportive. I have heard from others, and I am paraphrasing - 'I was raised in a belief system that god and his messengers are the only ones who have the power to heal and no one else.' That's perfectly fine too, and there is nothing wrong with that. When you learn the art of healing, and everyone can heal, you may run into a little resistance, and that's okay too.

Don't force anything on anyone, don't tell anyone that they are incorrect, and avoid trying to change someone's mind. If there are any changes that need to be made, they have to do it for themselves. If their beliefs are different than yours, you should respect that, and hopefully they respect yours. Some folks may fear your abilities since it is an unknown to them, so I would proceed with caution and avoid any confrontations with mixing Qigong and religion. It is better to walk away and become non-resistant then trying to battle over what is right and wrong.

I would recommend while teaching the class (unless you know everyone in the audience and their belief system) that it is not focused on any particular religion. You can talk about other non-specifics, but don't get into great detail. For example, when I talk about drawing upon your master's energy, I don't talk about specifics. I just say "Draw upon someone who is pure love, like a spiritual figure, a relative, a religious figure, or someone you trust". I make no mention of any exact denomination, I keep it generalized. Let people come to their own conclusions in their minds.

Many of us, have certain beliefs and don't want others telling us to convert and believe in something we don't. What I love about Qigong, is that it is not based or focused on any religion. It is something for everyone no matter who you are.

Before I go around the room and work with people's energy, I tell them that I will be walking around and balancing their energy. People accept that more than telling them that you will be doing 'healing energy' on them. So be careful in the words you choose for the group you will be working with.

KEEPING IT SOCIAL

One of the biggest downfalls of any group is lack of communication. After you've built your group, you need to maintain it. One of the most important things is to keep the lines of communications going between you and your students. Don't leave them hanging with a class just to attend, create some value behind it. To do so, think of ways to communicate with your students on days that you are not teaching class. For example, share an electronic newsletter. It doesn't have to be fancy, but something that continues to share the wealth that Qigong has to offer.

If you decide to send out information, do it on a regular basis and when people expect it. Don't overwhelm them with newsletters every week, space it out over a month or so. You don't have to spend a lot of time on it, meaning, don't put so much time into it that it takes valuable time away from others. I once did a weekly newsletter and it took 5-10 hours a week to put it together. I had to write the stories, find others to backfill the empty spaces, and depend on them to get it to me on time. Sometimes they could not meet the deadlines. Doing it once a month is fine.

Just imagine putting yourself into the shoes of others, how many emails do they get a day? How many other newsletters do they receive? With our digital age, it is very easy to get overwhelmed with too much information. A short newsletter that grabs their attention, one that they can't wait for the next one to come out.

Inform your group of other Qigong or holistic events in the area, become a resource for them. One they would appreciate and share amongst their friends and families. Do something that will build a relationship away from your regular practice. Maybe work with another practice group and practice Qigong together or do some healing on each other. Create something that people don't just attend, but are a part of the group.

If you have important information that needs to be sent out that is time-sensitive, like an upcoming event, class, seminar, etc., don't send it out the day before it happens. I have seen this too many times. Your attendance will be slim to none. Give people advance notice. They are not going to be on your website all the time looking at your schedule, they have schedules of their own. Help them out by reminding them at least a week or two in advance. Then send out a few reminders in between. They want to attend, but may have forgotten that email, and then boom, they got another and decided to sign up before forgetting again. Remember, repetition builds retention.

MEETING STUDENTS OUTSIDE OF PRACTICE

While your group is increasing with participants and your own personal network is also growing, you will eventually be bumping into people that are in your class or have taken your overview class and workshops. During the conversations, never interject "I haven't seen you in class for a while", or "Hope to see you in class soon" or "Are you going to be in class this week?"

Whatever you say around this topic is going to sound pushy. I would recommend that you never bring it up. Understand that people have busy lifestyles and may not be as dedicated to Qigong as you are. If they are meant to be there, they will be attending. You can make people feel really uncomfortable if you hint around the topic of attendance in your practice group, they may feel pressured.

You may lose a student, or they may share their uncomfortable experience with others in the group. Find other topics besides Qigong, unless it is brought up by them. Don't embarrass or pressure your students. Always make them feel welcome if they choose to attend.

Qigong is a choice and no one should feel pressured,

uncomfortable, or guilty. They should feel at peace with it, and attend whenever they want.

WORKING WITH THOSE WITH DISABILITIES

You may get the wonderful opportunity to work with people who have disabilities someday. To practice Qigong with those with challenges is such a beautiful experience. You will have a lot of fun, make some really great friends, and learn more about yourself in the process. If you never had the opportunity, I would suggest trying it. Working with such awesome people can change your life. You may even think that this could be challenging for yourself in teaching classes, and it may be at times, but don't worry, you'll have a great time doing it. It's a wonderful thing to see improvements, to hear stories from people who attend your class, and listen to them share their experiences.

I notice that some people feel a little uneasy when they are in a situation where they are face to face with people who seem to look out of their element, or function differently than themselves. In some cases, this may create a fear for those who have no exposure or experience in this area, they may be dealing with something in their minds as being labeled as unknown territory, and could seem threatening. No worries. Just keep in mind that we are all the same, we all have different challenges in our lives, and we work with them the best we can.

As a disabled military veteran myself, along with multiple injuries I have collected throughout my life (some that have stayed with me over the years), I still consider myself very fortunate, even though at times it can become a struggle and a blessing. Running a group like this can keep you on your toes, and you may not have a normal routine from one week to the next. Just enjoy the challenges and this will turn into something great for you. I myself have a great time, enjoy the conversations, hear about the accomplishments in people's lives, and most of all, share the love and energy in class.

When teaching Qigong in this area, each time is going to be different. You may have someone who is wheelchair bound, not able to move their limbs, cannot focus due to their ailment, and may not look like they are having a good time since they cannot copy your movements. I tell my audience that if they have limited or no mobility when doing the exercises, just imagine in your mind that you are performing them.

With practice, this can be very powerful for them. Depending on your situation, there may be a physical therapist or a loved one who would help move their arms for them to try and mimic the motions that you are doing. There is no reason to feel embarrassed or guilty when some of your students are not able to move their limbs, or even unable to touch their tongue to the roof of their mouth during the meditation. It will all work out in the end. Energy is intelligent and it will find its way to where it needs to go. I had one student who was very limited in their wheelchair and even though they could not do the movements, they really enjoyed the meditation. This was the best part of the class for them.

Another person whom I worked with was also limited in their wheelchair. They could not move their feet and had limited head and arms mobility. So what do you do at this point? What exercises should you choose? How do you fill an hour of time with very limited exercises?

These were the questions that ran through my mind, especially with class starting within a minute (I was late to class due to a snow storm that turned a 20 minute drive into an hour drive). I had to race through my memory on which Qigong moves would be the best in this situation. I chose the ones that did not use leg movements, and ones that worked with limited arm movements.

I had to extend some of the time with the exercises, but we got through it. After 30 minutes, I could tell he was getting tired, so I went into the meditation, which would give him time to relax. We ended about doing 50 minutes, so it wasn't a full hour, but that's okay. When you come into situations like these, it's okay to modify things so others can adapt.

Just go with the flow and teach as you always do, no matter who you are teaching, listen to your heart and your higher-self. It will guide you in many situations. Depending on who's attending, you may have to quickly learn from your audience what their limitations are and pick the Qigong exercises accordingly. If you have just wheel chair bound people who are very limited, you may do just a few exercises. They may not be able to move their legs, and be very limited in the arms. You may have to be quick on your feet and figure this out, or prepare yourself ahead of time so you have a list of what to teach.

If you make mistakes, that's okay. Just learn from them and move on. I have had many instances where I had to fine-tune my teachings due to my students' circumstances. People will really enjoy what you teach, especially if you treat them as equals. If you need to, grab a wheel chair, or a chair with arms, and figure out what exercises would work best for the audience before you teach.

In my practice groups, I get people who can stand, or they may have a walker, a wheel chair, or just be unable to stand for short or long periods of time. When I teach, it can be a different group, with the same people or a mixture, and they all come from different walks of life with different types of ailments. Every time it is a different experience, but I meet some wonderful people, and we have a great time.

Note: If you work in an environment where patients are being brought to your session, make sure that people understand that whoever attends should be willing to be there. I have had one instance where a patient is dropped off by one of the staff and left. They had no idea why they were there, and they felt very uncomfortable. Since the patient did not want to be there, they wanted to leave, and could not leave on their own. They also expressed that they were in pain, so I had to get someone to assist and leave my session to help this person.

I have had some dedicated people who work with their patients, especially if they have limited mobility. That staff member would help move the patient's arms during the exercises, and stay with them during the entire time. I find that very commendable, caring, and compassionate. If they feel like this is not for them, then they indicate this to the staff, and they can leave. Feel free to share this example if you will be working with patients. This will help keep the flow of the class going without interruption.

Remember to always have a backup plan and try to prepare as well as possible. Situations may arise where you are glad that you brought that extra something that saved the day. Good luck to those who work with those with challenges, I thank you and your students also thank you for taking your valuable time and spending it with them. It is greatly appreciated by all and I believe it will be rewarding to you as well.

THE NUMBER NINE

When I started out learning Qigong, I always heard the number nine. It was used everywhere. So I didn't understand it. I thought maybe eight was the high number somehow, but taking it to nine was just one more notch on some scale and it would take you just a little bit higher for better results. Why not take it to ten? Ten's a good number.

I didn't really know, but while I pondered it, the movie Spinal Tap popped into my thoughts. It was the scene where Nigel Tufnel is being interviewed, and he talks about his special amp. The volume goes to 11, while regular amps go to 10. The question comes up during the interview if having just one more notch on the amp makes the amp louder. The answer from Nigel – and I am paraphrasing from the movie, "It's one louder. Most blokes would be playing at 10........When we need that extra push over the cliff, we put it at 11.... one louder". So with this strange philosophy in mind, are we trying to max out and going to the highest level possible by going to 9 in Qigong, or should we take it up one more notch and go for 10? Making it just "one louder". As you can see, I love cult classic movies.

I needed to find the right answers since questions like this will come up while teaching. Quoting from the movie Spinal Tap, will not be giving the right answer in this situation, it will produce some blank stares, and people may think that I may need to be admitted. Remember, don't make things up, and take note from your students. If you don't know the answer, no worries, just tell them you will find the answer and get back to them. I decided to find this answer for myself, so I met up with one of the staff members at the place where I learned Qigong, and I learned a lot from our conversation and wanted to share some of the content with you.

As was previously mentioned, the Number 9 is used frequently in Qigong. You may have noticed that it is used frequently in some of the exercises. Rubbing your ears on the count of nine, or combing the top of your head, or patting yourself down nine times. So let's take a look at the reason why this mysterious number nine is so important.

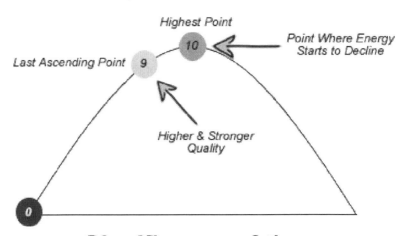

Signifigance of the Number Nine in Qigong

On a scale of 0-10, where zero is the lowest and ten is the highest in energy, you want to move to the last ascending point (9) in Qigong before you hit the highest point (10). When you take it to 10, this is where energy begins to drop. The quality of the energy at point 9, is at its highest and strongest. When the highest point (10) is reached, the energy starts to decline. This is the reason why nine is very important in working with energy. So there's the simplistic explanation.

WHAT TIME IS IT?

Places that you practice may not have a clock available on the wall. So be prepared. If you have a watch and check your wrist frequently, others may begin to think that you're in a rush for another pressing engagement and have lost focus with them. If you use the same space frequently to teach, purchase a wall clock (facing away from your Qigongers so that they are not distracted by the time) or have the facility put one up for you. Another tip is to use your smart phone.

You can download apps that can show an actual clock on your screen (digital or analog). I actually use one called "Clocks" that I found in the 'app store'. Depending on your phone's screen size, it can be an advantage or disadvantage. Mine is the perfect size and fits perfectly for my means. I will prop it up against something so that I can see it all the time. Some protective cases for the phone have a stand built into them or you can get an accessory that can mount your phone. Some you can adjust the angle to your liking. However you do it, it will be helpful so you can start and end your class on time.

I WANT TO HEAR FROM YOU!

Yes, I want to hear from you. I think that it's important to hear your opinion about this book to help others decide if this is the right book for them. What did you like or dislike about this book? Do you think the information provided here has or will be helpful in building a successful practice group? I definitely want to hear about it. How did this book impact you? Share your story.

I would like you to do me a great kindness and return to whichever website you ordered this book from. Make your comments about what you think about it. The reason I ask is that it is my goal to improve the quality of this book to help others like yourself continue spreading Qigong across the world. So at this very moment, while things are fresh in your mind, get on your computer, go to that website and write your review. Then I would like to deeply say thank you for your great kindness in doing so.

DOWNLOADABLE PRACTICE GROUP STARTER KIT

If you are interested in downloading the information mentioned in this book, please visit **Downloads.QigongWithJim.com**

The following is a list of materials to download in helping you organize and run a long term practice group.

- Two-hour PowerPoint Presentation - An overview of Qigong
- 30 Second Elevator Speech - Several 30 second snippets to help you prepare to answer questions about Qigong
- Checklists - All sorts of lists to keep you organized
- Do not disturb sign - To keep your group punctual
- Feedback forms - Forms to be filled out by students to provide feedback on your performance
- Fliers - Materials to place on bulletin boards or other places to gain some exposure
- Goal Setting for Practice Group Leaders - Help you focus on the present and future of your group
- Sample email announcements - To be sent to your prospects and current students
- Qigong daily workout sheet - Track your progress
- Tri-folds - Handouts about Qigong and your class
- Waivers for students - Legal paperwork to cover your assets
- Qigong Tips - Basic tips for students
- Testimonial Forms - Teaches your students how to write a phenomenal testimonial for you
- More signage - Guiding students to you in a building

Thank You

Again, thank you for reading this book and I hope the information presented to you helps you become successful in creating and maintaining your Qigong practice group.

© Copyright Notice

WEBSITES ASSOCIATED WITH THIS BOOK

www.QigongWithJim.com

This is a community website for Qigongers to post their practice groups, to support each other in sharing ideas and stories, download repository of documents, along with sharing stories and ideas.

Blog.QigongWithJim.com

This website is an extension of this book, where ideas continue to flow in helping people lead, build, and grow their practice group. Find out what others are doing and share your own experiences with others.

Here are some of the places mentioned in the book along with the websites/contact info of those who participated in this book.

Pathways Minneapolis
Pathways is a building, a space, and a community. It is a place set aside for exploring ways to come to holistic health through classes, special events, and individual sessions. By participating in the many free services at Pathways, you are supported in taking charge of your healing journey – wherever that may lead.
www.PathWaysMinneapolis.org

To contact Barb Palmer about her Qigong Practice Group at Pathways, email her at BarbQigong@live.com

----

About the VA Health Care System in Minneapolis:
VA Health Care System (VAHCS) is a teaching hospital providing a full range of patient care services with state-of-the-art technology, as well as education and research. Comprehensive health care is provided through primary care, tertiary care and long-term care in areas of medicine, surgery, psychiatry, physical medicine and rehabilitation, neurology, oncology, dentistry, geriatrics and extended care.
www.Minneapolis.VA.gov

Dayton's Bluff Seniors Living at Home / Block Nurse Program:
A non-profit community based service organization which operates with the financial support of our community; private and public agencies and foundations, local churches, neighbors and friends. We collaborate with community members and organizations to create and maintain resources to help seniors overcome barriers to remain living in their homes.
www.DaytonsBluffSeniors.org

Heart of Tao Resonance Art
A place for everyone to come to heal their body, mind and spirit, a place to practice and cultivate heart of Tao, and a place to express your being and create community of like-hearted people.
www.HotResonanceArt.com

Qigong For Balance
Arda's private healing practice, located in Palo Alto, CA, where he provides individual energy healing sessions and conducts workshops about personal and spiritual growth, negative life patterns and mindfulness. He also offers distant energy healing and mentoring sessions across the world.
Qigong4Balance.com

ABOUT THE AUTHOR

Jim Cormican is an entrepreneur, a business owner, a leader within his community, a visionary and an inspiration to others. After several life-changing events, Qigong found him at a crisis center in Minneapolis, Minnesota. While attending several classes, he was hooked on this ancient Chinese art from the Far East, and was very determined to learn more by seeking and receiving training on this mysterious and interactive therapy.

Mr. Cormican was inspired by many of the stories of people's struggles with dis-eases, and how Qigong has helped them. So Jim set out to meet the requirements to learn Qigong and created his own practice groups. He has reached out to countless people over the years where he has taught people in workshops, in their homes, medical centers, and in group settings. Jim (a disabled military veteran), currently volunteers his time in leading Qigong practice groups at the Veteran Administration Health Care System in Minneapolis, Minnesota. His Qigong practice groups work with military veterans who are at the center due to their illnesses, injuries, and disabilities.

Jim also consults others on their own Qigong practice groups and works with businesses to help improve or implement training programs related to teaching Qigong. You can find Jim online at **www.QigongWithJim.com** or follow his posts about practice groups at **Blog.QigongWithJim.com**

22580445R00096

Printed in Poland
by Amazon Fulfillment
Poland Sp. z o.o., Wrocław